MW00579897

SAN FRANCISCO WRITERS CONFERENCE

SFWriters.org

2022 Writing Contest Anthology

Everything Intensely

First Edition

Designed and Produced by E. A. Provost at
New Alexandria Creative Group
For the San Francisco Writers Conference Anthology
©Copyright 2022 by the San Francisco Writers Conference
All rights reserved by the individual authors.
www.NewAlexandriaCG.com
www.SFWriters.org
Available everywhere via print on demand.
Please support your local bookstores.
ISBN: 978-1-64715-005-1

Dear Reader,

The 2022 San Francisco Writers Conference Writing Contest brought out some interesting depths of contemplation in us. While the 2021 contest frequently ran to themes of social justice, 2022 entrants seemed to be largely about the losses we experience. Perhaps because we've lost so many loved ones in recent years. Perhaps because we've spent more time alone, experiencing our feelings without the usual distractions. No theme is assigned to this contest, so it's fascinating to see what themes emerge spontaneously and to consider what might inspire them.

Awarding a Grand Prize was particularly difficult. Each of the category winners hooked us. The vivid descriptions in *Mother* contrasted with the airy simplicity of *The Thin Man*, which strove to communicate the same emotion on a single page. They weighed against the interesting connections posited by *Fire in the Mind*. Even as adults, the middle-grade entry, *Broken Promises*, captured our interest as it delved into a time and perspective our school history books certainly overlooked. *Three Seconds;* gained a worthy Category Win when we elevated *Fire in the Mind* to Grand Prize Winner. We could remark on every finalist for some notable attribute, but you should read them yourself.

Fortunately, all of them are printed here, in our second contest anthology celebrating our 17th annual contest. Entries were limited to the first 1500 words of an unpublished or self-published manuscript or up to 3 poems (judged individually) with a collective word count within that. That's a generous chance to make a good first impression on an agent or editor, so this anthology is also an opportunity for aspiring writers to see what caught our agent judges.

CONGRATULATIONS! To each of the entrants published here and especially our Grand Prize and Category Winners. We hope this book will entice readers to seek out the work of our finalists as they achieve greater success in the coming years. Several 2021 finalists have already informed us that they've signed publishing deals or chosen to self-publish, and we can't wait to read their and your completed works.

THANK YOU! To every writer who submitted work, we cannot hold a writing contest without broad participation, and more and better-quality entries were submitted this year than ever. Your persistence as you continue to improve and submit is the critical factor in achieving success as an author, and we honor your efforts. To our volunteers and judges who made this contest happen. To New Alexandria Creative Group, who partnered with us to publish this beautiful anthology. The generosity of our community fills our hearts.

Sincerely,

The San Francisco Writers Conference Executive Board

Find out more about the San Francisco Writers Conference and our year-round events, including the next writing contest, at sfwriters.org.

TABLE OF CONTENTS

POETRY

CATEGORY WINNER:
THE THIN MAN
BY LEIGH LUCAS

The Thin Man

got so thin

I could count his ribs;

I'd coax him
To eat,

I

Unable to inspire

The man I love

To take care
Of himself,

He

Who never worried

About his health,

the one   who

got   to   disappear

Leigh Lucas is a poet and writer in San Francisco. Winner of AWP's 2020 Kurt Brown Prize for an emerging poet, 2022 Best of the Net nominee, and 2021 Pushcart Prize nominee. She has been awarded residencies at Tin House, Sewanee, Community of Writers, and Kenyon. Her poems appear in and are forthcoming from *Smartish Pace, Minnesota Review, Frontier Poetry,* and *Poet Lore.* You can read her work at LeighLucas.com.

A WARRIOR NONETHELESS
BY HANNAH WATSON

A Warrior Nonetheless

Fragile voicemail,
Hurried footsteps,
The suction of sliding doors,
Grant passage to a white room
with a clock that's ticking
but not keeping time.
It's four hours off, I think,
but what matters when one's horizon
is nothing but windowless walls.

She lies there
propped up, head back,
eyes to the heavens,
but closed resolutely.
Jaw clenched, face braced,
she's locked in combat
somewhere within,
waging war against a victor
who already wears the crown.
Outnumbered and surrounded,
she'll go down
a warrior, nonetheless.

Doctors deal out half measures
in tranquilizing tones,
turn to those of us still standing,
as if soothing a toddler's tantrum.

Hope, futility, strategy, surrender,
all weaved together,
and cloaked around our shoulders
with such empathy.
His subdued voice wields the scalpel,
expert precision splices the question,
speaking truth without stating
what clearly lies in waiting.
Careful not to poke the bruise
that can't be covered up.

She looks small, stretched thin,
Like the paper sheet she's wrapped in.
Unfamiliar yet recognizable,
she used to be indomitable.
All my life a force large and looming,
a rage coiled back, a strength unmoving.
She would fight to the last man.

She turns toward my father,
head bowed, still
yielding no ground.
Grasps his hand, pulls him closer,
forehead to forehead, he leans over,
shuts his eyes to the world,
we're in this together.
Their breath falls silently in step,
with the count
of the clock
on the wall.

Hannah Watson lives in Atlanta, Georgia. Having raised a family and worked in the legal field, she is taking a pause to explore new ventures. This is her first published work.

ALONE IN SAN FRANCISCO
BY LALIT KUMAR

Alone in San Francisco

Sauntering down the Embarcadero
Along the edges of pier 39,
A foggy morning clings to the city,
Rumbling itself awake from slumber.

I trudge along the wooden pier,
The waves lap at the jetty
The winds howl in my ears
A pelican nonchalantly flaps its wings
And flies past my view ahead.

It's not so lonely, after all
The nature is resplendent in its spread today,
The winds, the waves, the ocean
Seem to have no bearing
To the seasons of my mind.
Nature is constant,
My mind shifts with each seed of thought.

I am not so lonely, after all
I open my arms
To welcome the oncoming wind
feeling it directly on my face.
I let it caress
My skin and my face
I feel it ruffle my hair,
And I close my eyes to
Witness the love of my friend.

I jump in the oncoming waves
The blues of Pacific
Is as cold as
The thaw in my heart.
It's an instant commingling
Of two long lost lovers
For whom
The distance has not dimmed
The light of their hearts.

Distant memory
Has a way of its own
To ebb and flow with the tide.
A dream
Can rise aflutter with the waves
Or sink to the bottom
With the changing tides
And time.

The ocean water,
I feared it may drown me,
Instead taught me how to
Swim with the tide.

Lalit Kumar works in the Technology sector in the SF Bay area and likes to write around the themes of adventure and travel. His recently published poetry book *Years Spent: Exploring Poetry in Adventure, Life and Love*, is among top three Selects in the Poetry genre for 'Indie Spotlight' by Publishers Weekly, July 25th, 2022. He writes a monthly column in 'India Currents' magazine called 'Road Raves' sharing his passion for high-adventure sports. Find him on Instagram, @lalitk06 or his website at lalitkumaronline.com

DRUNK BUDDHA
BY JEFF WALT

Drunk Buddha

Here on the corner of Manic & Depressed, some dude
looks like he's perpetually scoring at pinball—all fists, hump thrusts, *Fuck!*
& green neck veins swollen & stretching when he wallops the air
waiting for the bus that never comes. Or comes & goes without anyone.

The Buddha tattooed on his forehead is crying & holds a Bud.
On bruised stick legs, paces furiously in unlaced work boots
& see-through white tennis shorts: "The end of the world!" he proclaims—
pulsing a vehement middle finger to the sky—is only days away.

In my window seat at my favorite café, I stare back at my seven-dollar Chai
for guidance, wondering if the foam the barista etched
is a wilting pansy, a shooting penis, or a Bodhi tree ablaze?
I want my money's worth from this drink. I want a vision:

I want my foam to churn a third eye that winks back flirtatiously
or the Bhagavad Gita's wispy spelling out the answer
to what it means to be alive & dying
because I believe my street prophets. I believe, too, the snap

of the bug light behind me—that drives me crazy—is a warning
as it zaps the stupid, trapped flies & startles me
like that seven second earthquake that threw everything I owned
across the room. My old Buddhist friend once told me

here are tiny deaths all around us each day, and now I see them:
look at the Asian Lady Liberty Mutual ad spinning her giant, zany
arrow at the intersection that points toward
How much I will get back? A tiny death. *And when?* Another.

We can pop shark cartilage, rhino tusk, hit the oxygen bar
downtown for doubles of my favorite cotton candy flavor
while we get a mani-pedi. We can pop up
to Disneyland & give ourselves the stuffed Dumbo

we never got as a child. We can finally get it up
with that blue pill even when we masturbate, so we feel
more attractive in the world. Tomorrow I will start day one at the gym.
I will pick up the thread & needle & mend each torn item in my life,

maybe. Perhaps I will buy the bovine afterbirth on eBay
to naturally tighten my skin. I will definitely install that outdoor camera
with night vision. I will see what needs to be seen. See what scrounges and scurries
in the night. I will confront my old therapist

who said he wouldn't be sitting in a room with me if he'd been better
at organic chemistry. He's calm for a second, my messed-up Buddha:
stands defiantly now & stares his best beast down, lip twitching,
then pulls his zipper down up down up down up down up down

like a fierce & magical instrument he's mastered
& his music is a weapon with a kind, vengeful melody.

Jeff Walt has published in *Los Angeles Review, Alligator Juniper, Cimarron Review, The Sun, Connecticut Review, Inkwell, New Millennium Writings, The Good Men Project, Harpur Palate, Cream City Review, The Ledge,* and *Slipstream*. His book, *Leave Smoke,* was published on Oct. 1, 2019, by Gival Press and was awarded the 2020 Housatonic Book Award given by the Western Connecticut State University MFA Program "…to promote excellent writing, to identify authors who serve as professional role models for writing students." *Leave Smoke* was awarded Runner-Up in Poetry in the 2020 San Francisco Book Festival annual competition honoring the best books of the spring. JeffWalt.com

FORGED BY FLAME
BY DANIEL MORESCHI

Forged by Flame

A shroud of crowded canopies impedes
The vital touch of Summer-morning's gaze
From animating barred, deprived arrays
Of shrubs and saplings flanked by stranded seeds.

This sacred, sylvan paradise grows dry
And bare. The understories start to fail
And only roots of yesterdays prevail
At fronts, where even timeless borders die.

Once lofty layers part, the leafy screen
Is breached by glimmers of candescent streaks
Like sunlit lances falling from the peaks
To grace the gapes and greenage with a sheen…

A soil-stoked flash pervades a forest floor
And in its wake, a smoldering refrain;
A blackened arc, and then a crimson vein
Protrudes where sheltered embers pulse and pour.

An all-consuming current swiftly sweeps
Decayed debris; a glade of graves that spurs
This fervid force. It grows until it stirs
With homing heaves that skim the rims of steeps.

A wind-borne flurry mounts the mounds and smites

The trunks of lonesome pines, before it sets

And elevates with blazing pirouettes:

A coup that climbs the crowns and claims the heights.

As dens and havens wane, a spate of quakes

Reverberate: A flood of fauna braves

A baleful labyrinth of amber waves

Amid nigrescent clouds and singeing lakes.

The morrows slowly ease their tempered strife

When hazy frays abate. A stillness comes:

No forlorn calls are heard, nor thudding thrums,

Nor morning songs, nor flights. No signs of life.

And in an ashen aftermath, the earth

Looks scorched and lusterless, devoid of dews.

But tasteless shades in place of vibrant hues

Belie a subtle cycle of rebirth.

A burst of verdant filaments ascends

From blackened barks, and luscious tufts abound

From buried buds on desecrated ground:

Their new beginnings forged by stricken ends.

Daniel Moreschi is a poet from Neath, South Wales, UK. After life was turned upside down by his ongoing battle with severe M.E., he rediscovered his passion for poetry which had been dormant since his teenage years. Daniel has been acclaimed by many poetry competitions, including those hosted by: Oliver Goldsmith Literature Festival, Wine Country Writers Festival, Ohio Poetry Day, Westmoreland Arts & Heritage Festival, and Short Stories Unlimited. Daniel has also had poetry published by *The Society of Classical Poets*, and *The Black Cat Poetry Press*. Find him on Instagram at @ daniel.moreschi

Hell 'n' Back
by Jehr Schiavo

Hell 'n' Back

I'd always been struck whenever noticing somebody who didn't have a place to live, wondering how they became homeless.

That first homeless person I encountered was in 1977, on Grant Avenue near Geary and Market St., at the Wells Fargo entrance in San Francisco.

An early morning on my way to open Vidal Sassoon, halfway through my year-long apprenticeship.

The man passed on the sidewalk wore multiple pairs of pants and a few overcoats. What piqued my curiosity was what appeared to be black soot on the man's only exposed skin, his face and hands.

Three years ago, lying down in some abandoned house's yard, I reached behind my neck to scratch my shoulder blade with nails I hadn't cut in months.

While scratching myself, I felt a thick oily substance collecting underneath my jagged nails.

Inspecting them afterward, I noticed black soot.

From what I remembered, caked on the man's face and hands forty-two years earlier on the sidewalk, in front of that Wells Fargo bank, across the street from Vidal Sassoon.

Which brought to mind the question I needed to answer…

'Is this the way you want to die?'

A favorite of my childhood memories hanging out with my mother, Jean, was spent after dinner when Mom told me stories about her life.

Being myself, a curious twelve-year-old

didn't bother to think before opening my mouth.

'Mom, how'd you get that scar on your forehead?'

"Tony hit me in the head with a Coke bottle."

Tony is the father of my two older sisters.

When Mom was finished explaining how Tony abused her, I asked the obvious question,

Why didn't she take her two daughters and leave?

My heart sank, hearing Jean's reply.

"Because, he said if I left him and took the girls, he would come looking for me,

along with them, and kill us all".

Lacking a solid plan to escape five years of abuse, Jean knocked on a convent door.

Since childhood, she dreamt of becoming a nun long before her dreadful arranged marriage to Tony.

A dark place in Jean's life, when she left her daughters behind, as she couldn't see another solution to getting pummeled — other than being

a homeless woman on the streets of Newark, New Jersey, in 1956.

Jean's next reality check, one I find difficult to imagine, was what she went through facing the light of day when she opened those convent doors after being rejected by the Mother Superior.

My father lied through his teeth to befriend my mother.

Had Mom been aware that my father was married and had an eight-year-old daughter,

she would not have given him the time of day.

Months after they met, on occasion to inform my father that Jean was pregnant with his child (me), he stuck out his hand and said… "Good luck."

I knew there wasn't a father.

The man I wanted to call Dad lived somewhere across two rivers in New Jersey.

He'd show up now and then: a couple days stubble, pack of Camel straights, and a quart of Schaefer beer.

Sometimes spending a few hours as planned; other times, he wouldn't show, as not planned.

Six decades later…

While rats nibbled me past midnight, tossing, turning, trying to sleep on concrete, I understood without a shadow of a doubt that there was no place lower I could possibly go.

Without a roof, running water, or electricity, existence held little promise other than the deepest contemplation I'd ever known.

I'm pleased to say that end of my world isn't any longer a slow death.

My worthiness was raised significantly.

Gratitude, along with a sense of being humble, grabbed me by the hand and pulled me back among the living.

On a Spring day, strolling around Castellammare del Golfo, my daughter, walking in the middle between the former spouse and myself, heard my daughter blurt, "Poppi, you're not gonna like where we're going."

We continued along, allowing a minute or so to pass, letting it sink in.

Then asked her, 'Where you goin'?'

Without apparent care, she announced," We're moving to Grandma and Grandpa's!"

Several weeks later, two days after returning to San Francisco from Sicily,

the former spouse and our daughter parted company with me at Hotel Kabuki.

Formerly, the Miyako Hotel, where the Sex Pistols had their final fiasco,

turned into my 'hell.'

Sixteen years, as Famiglia di Schiavo, became our last night together there too.

No more wife, muse, business partner, best friend, lover — or precious, intuitive whip-smart, sensitive, beautiful daughter.

Unprepared, mentally and emotionally, I fell into pieces, unable to get back up.

Both hands started trembling, and simultaneously I began to experience an alarming amount of weight loss.

My body started to eat itself (almost overnight), morphing into skin and bones.

Clients couldn't bear their appointments with me — demand vanished.

Two months after our separation, the former spouse drove my daughter forty miles from Irvine to visit me while I had a break from cutting clients at the Hyatt LAX.

My daughter appeared much older, new to wearing makeup, once a little girl — became a distant impression.

The former spouse couldn't stomach me, period.

In the interim of those first two months apart, she had already moved on, by then living with her new boyfriend.

They met on our fifteenth wedding anniversary.

Weeks later, I bought a Gillette razor cartridge at an Oakland CVS as a last resort and flew back to Los Angeles.

With a drained bank account, I thought about being homeless in LA and decided instead to take an Uber to Union Station, boarding an Amtrak Surfliner headed for San Diego.

Sunk further and further over the next few months. Which included several weeks in a psych ward.

Unlike Iggy Pop's looney bin accommodations, with David Bowie and Dennis Hopper supplying Iggy cocaine galore.

An explanation soon arrived as to why my hands trembled, alongside the sudden weight loss.

I was diagnosed with Graves Disease, an immune disorder of the thyroid.

They released me six weeks later.

Flat broke, I crashed at the youngest of my two older sisters' condo.

Which was doomed to fail given our stormy history.

After that scenario deteriorated, I checked into San Diego's wide-open streets.

Didn't get in touch with more than a couple of friends throughout that grim stretch.

Completely humiliated, alongside figuring there wasn't much anyone could say or do other than feeling powerless over my situation.

A makeshift homeless shelter during the Pandemic Lockdown at San Diego's Convention Center, housing five-hundred men to each section, was a repulsive mistake.

Alternated use between one of two men's bathrooms, having eight urinals and four toilets, smeared with human excrement, blended by dark amber urine.

Early osteoporosis, caused by Graves Disease, escalated to multiple compression fractures on my vertebrae.

Doctors aren't able to pinpoint why my bones can't retain calcium.

I was admitted to UCSD's emergency room in July 2021. Wheeled up to their ICU, over the next few days, given an ultrasound, EKG, CT scan, and MRI.

All to find a blood clot in my right leg, with more on my lung.

Hours later, the radiology department slipped me some fentanyl through a drip, jabbed me with sufficient lidocaine, inserted a Denali IVC filter through the jugular, guiding it into my stomach, preventing the leg's blood clot from rising before reaching my heart.

An emergency contact at UCSD was my other (well-balanced) eldest sister.

A week after being admitted, she and her husband were there to pick me up after being discharged.

My brother-in-law presented two options: "You can go back on the street or come to the house."

I gotta say this; it's quite the surreal experience going from dying on the street to being around family who care about me.

My soon-to-be nineteen-year-old daughter

can't wrap her head around how I let life spiral so out of control.

Being swayed by her mother's biased notions is an understatement.

As I've mentioned earlier, and I can't express this enough, two important lessons were learned during those three years on the street.

Both I had always understood the definition of, though neither believed pertained to me.

The first is gratitude, the other to remain humble in the worst and best of times.

It's thirteen months since I'm off the street and out of hospitals.

Living with my sister and her husband for four months, another two months in Manhattan, five months staying in Carrizalillo, and two in Sicily.

I had beat myself up sufficiently throughout those homeless years.

In time, I forgave myself, the former spouse, and my daughter.

Every last drop of grieving, losing my family and our life together, ran its nasty course.

These days, whenever I come across a homeless person, I no longer wonder how they managed to get into their particular situation.

I presume they're battling varying degrees of a thorny past.

Jehr Schiavo, a celebrated individualist-hairstylist-raconteur, began his revolutionary ride four decades ago in San Francisco. A nonfiction beauty, health, and awareness manifesto, *Mr. Haute Coiffure* pierces the underbelly of a beauty industry unchecked, while denouncing associated corporate overlords. Presently, he continues writing while traveling between delivering sustainable Jehrcuts to select patrons who commission him in Los Angeles, San Francisco, and New York.

"It's okay, Mom"
by Sharon Harris

It's okay, Mom

I looked up to my mom
She was beautiful with high cheek bones and long brown hair
I watched her come out of her room with a new fit and do
Make up on, hair and dress on fleek. I love you,
But You don't love me
It's plain to see, by the way you treat me
Like I'm less than a princess
Less than your baby Queen
But It's okay mom. I understand you did the best you could with what you knew
And for that, I've always forgiven you
A child raising a child
Trying to be the most loving mother after being defiled
Not knowing your rights,
You surrendered to a losing fight
You never loved yourself. So how could you possibly love me?
All you know is disrespect and beatings
So that's the love you've been delivering
But it's okay mom. It's okay
It's okay because, I don't blame you
How could you possibly know how to keep me safe when you married the monster
who controlled you and taught you that disfunction was love?
But, it's okay mom. I forgive you.
I forgive you for loving a man more than your namesake
I forgive you for not protecting me or my sisters
How could you give what you didn't possess?
I wished upon a star that you would find a way to leave
I always wished you had enough strength keep us all safe,
But wishing on a star has never given me a return on my investment
Through age eighteen I lived in silent stress
But it's okay mom.
It's okay that I never experienced security in love

It's okay because, I looked to men for love
Used and abused because that's what I learned from you
I gave birth to two girls and I was determined to show them what unconditional
love is
I made sure to hug them and tell them that I love them
But You know what mom? Your lack of love is being passed down through
generations
Now your grand babies views are being tainted.
Distorted, because I don't love all of me truly
How could I when I never learned it, never felt it, never possessed it.
It's okay.
I'll keep telling myself it's okay until I believe it because you know what mom?
It's not okay. It's not okay that you chose a man over your daughters and self but,
I forgive you anyway

Army Veteran and chef, **Sharon Harris**, enjoys writing in a variety of mediums such as screenplays, poetry, and dramatic novels. Sharon derives pleasure in taking long walks on the beach, as well as relishing in exquisite sunsets from coast to coast. Across every continent, she aspires to leave her footprints in search of the most delicious sunset the eyes can feast on. She shares her innermost thoughts on both Instagram, @ authorsharonharris, and her website, sharonsgroovylife.com.

LAST DAY OF PROPHECY SEASON
BY CHRISTY WISE

Last Day of Prophecy Season

I

Dawn breaks late. Grass dormant, Winter stones,
cold. Delphi's summer heat, evanescent.

Pythia brews tea, walks at a deliberate
pace, wraps herself in violet shawl and slippers.

She dreads the icy, hard tripod, her daylong perch.

Gilded brass, all show. Faux finery. If their worship
were true, her seat would be padded, covered with Egyptian linen.

Many of Pythia's attendants are gone. Apollo's chariot is packed,
ready for summer frolic among the Hyperboreans.

Voices carry across chilled air. Pythia sips mountain tea,
eyes close, insides warm. She sets the pace.

II

Hey, man, whose idea is this? Pay drachmas, climb
craggy path in frozen daybreak to listen -- to what?

A crazy woman on a bronze tripod proffers
predictions? As if she knows, as if anyone knows.

Charade. And everyone plays along. If I don't,
my reputation tarnishes. What this money could buy,

makes me cry. Instead: expensive ambiguities.
Your future could be this, possibly that.

Pick one, lady. Earn your bribe. People shove,
yell, barter for a place in front. I hope time

runs out before I reach the top. I'll take my offering,
buy a warm jacket, drink sweet wine.

Christy Wise is a poet, essayist, and author. Her poems have appeared in *Evening Street Press, Anthem,* and *Upside Down and From Below: Marin Poetry Center Anthology 2022,* among others. Christy is co-author of *A Mouthful of Rivets: Women at Work in World War II.* Her essay, *Memory Book* was a notable essay in *Best American Essays 2010.* She feels most at home walking along the Pacific Ocean and hiking in Desolation Wilderness. ChristyWise.com.

LUNCH WITH MY ACCOUNTANT
BY KENNETH E. BAKER

Lunch with My Accountant

Burrito or bowl?
  how many times I remembered to water the plants
Pork, beef, or vegetarian?
Black or red beans?
  the number of times I smiled at a stranger
Lettuce?
Spicy or mild?
  how many times I pleasured my partner
Sour Cream?
Guacamole?
Do I want a drink?
  how many times I pleasured myself

Lunch order conundrums
  number of times I tipped the right amount
the mouth awaits with watery anticipation.
  number of times a good friend was chosen
A proper solution then lunch is good,
  how many times I ate a healthy lunch
otherwise another meh added to the meh tally
  number of laughs I got with a bad pun
kept in the back of mind along with all the other tallies
  number of times I laughed alone
stored and stacked.
  how many times I ate alone
      at a table filled with people

My internal accountant never sleeps
how many times was kindness chosen
counting each moment's choice
how many times was selfishness chosen
occasionally submitting a status report.
number of times I called my mother

I wake up feeling down
number of times I told my son "I love you"
judgement unconsciously rendered.
number of times I called myself stupid
My day is filled with stiletto comments,
number of times I called myself stupid
passing papercuts of apathetic cruelty.
number of times I called myself

I decide lunch will be a veggie bowl with black beans,
spicy salsa, lettuce, and guac…

Maybe lunch will be good…

Maybe tomorrow will be a good day.

Kenneth E Baker has assumed the roles of landlord, triathlete, composer, handyman, father, fencer, data security specialist, and life coach. He brings all these experiences into his eclectic sensibility when writing poetry. His work has been included in *orangepeel literary magazine*, *OpenDoor Magazine*, and *Storytelling Collective's Collective Verses | Volume I*.

POETRY ON THE MOON
BY SADIE MILLER

Poetry on the Moon

scenic views make me scream

standing on a precipice
beauty just out of reach.

it's no wonder wolves scream at the moon
begging
pleading
come closer.
But you can't hear screams on the moon.

have you ever longed to throw yourself into a divine canyon
if only to fly for a moment?
become the earth
decorate rocks with red and sunshine.
I could write an elegy to myself in red
and it would be exquisite.

I'm blessed to bleed uncut
for my moon
and still she keeps her distance.

Would she lean in for a joke?
KNOCK KNOCK

But you can't hear knocking on the moon.
You can't hear "let me in" on the moon.
You can't hear *bitch* or *too late* on the moon.

You can't hear transplanted shame on the moon.

You can't hear curses and prophecies on the moon.
You can't hear "you'll die in your sleep" on the moon.
You can't hear a matter of time on the moon.
You can't hear "you don't try" on the moon.
You can't hear too big to small too dirty too vain too
smart too stupid too tall too loud too quiet

too feminine too sad too angry too happy too bubbly
too young too old too proud too insecure

too hysterical too cold on the moon
can't hear on the moon

Sadie Miller spent her childhood in the Bay Area writing stories and running them past her Shih Tzu, Zsa Zsa. Now, she's a student at UC Berkeley (where Zsa Zsa can visit). She explores her experiences and whimsies through her lifelong passion for writing, immortalizing her tales of femininity, body image, superb dragons, and mental health. Her work can be found on her Instagram and TikTok @eucatasadie.

THE LAST TIME I SAW MY BROTHER
BY CONSTANCE HANSTEDT

The last time I saw my brother

he opened his screen door
and I took him all in—blue-gray eyes,
half-smile, freshly shaven face, slippers worn
yet sturdy. We hugged and I patted
the soft plane just beneath his shoulders,
wondering why he wore a sweatshirt
on the balmy Florida morning.

He'd been our Christmas miracle.
After months of constant pain,
steroids, and delusions, he sat on
the salmon-colored sofa with his feet
firmly planted on the wood floor.
I chose my words carefully at first
until his brows relaxed, remembering
fragments of what we had shared.

I recalled our evenings when
I was in college, and he had dropped out,
when over beer and pizza, we dreamt
of where we'd be in ten years.
It had been a continuous theme—
him, moving west in a Buick
named Thunder with tires spinning
and "Brown Sugar" blasting,
and me, a reliable job, a little money,
babies perhaps, and a two-story house
beneath a lemon dab of moon.

How easy it was then, unaware
of the sheer force of what waited ahead.

He stood and considered if we should go
to lunch, conscious of crowds,
air contaminated with germs,
grimy fingerprints on tables and doors.

There is a heaviness in the plain truth.
Acceptance, a tequila-laced burning
in our throats.

Constance Hanstedt is the author of the memoir *Don't Leave Yet, How My Mother's Alzheimer's Opened My Heart* (She Writes Press, 2015), and the poetry chapbook *Treading Water* (Finishing Line Press, 2022). Her poetry explores the integral aspects of family, loss, redemption, and compassion. Constance is on the executive board of the California Writers Club and its branch, Tri-Valley Writers, where she leads a dynamic poetry critique group. Find her online at ConstanceHanstedt.com.

WORDS
BY MICHAEL MILLER

words

yes, perhaps i compliment you too much,
like each time your eyes, seriously bright,
catch me up, carry me to your calm touch
where words tread soft against your dream world's light.
the breezy way your sweet philosophy,
like rain's fresh fall, clears harsh winter away,
finds me in awe of love's grand potency,
where caught by your gaze i willingly stay.
the wonder is this joy is possible,
against the longing want that love's pain knows.
as you walk towards me, irresistible,
your smile forgives the past regrets i chose.
　　how ever much my words put you at ease,
　　they merely reflect how your eyes can please.

a sonnet over dinner
(on rue saint denis)

i don't know the ways i miss you until
struck again before i know what hit me
i see a dress you would perfectly fill
though you've yet to find love a certainty.
i sit here dining as sparrows flit through,
and try to glimpse your beauty sitting there.
the songs they chirp are what i'm left in lieu
of what i wish from you in our affair.

still, though you choose to hold yourself aloof,
i know if you would let me in your heart
you'd find my gentle touch would give you proof
that passion's climax is a simple art.
   you rouse in me a love to satisfy
    the depth we'd find in ecstasy's slow sigh.

stray

at times some nights your sweetness showed a way
you didn't even have awareness of.
i touched you gently and your hand would stray
to find my hand as if there might be love.
the cool, spring night we walked along broadway
amidst gay pride, punk rock and the artists,
you leaned against me as if you might stay
and trust a chance at love your life resists.
your body spoke what you did not admit,
that you were touched by love for a moment.
though our two lives could never find a fit,
my memory of that night is content
   to see the burdened past fall from your eye
    and, with simple touch, to my love reply.

Michael Miller lives in Edmonds, WA on the Puget Sound with his wife and their two cats. In 2022, Michael received an honorable mention in the Yeats Society of New York's Poetry Prize. His poems have appeared in the New Guard Review, Lyric Magazine, The Society of Classical Poets, and others.

THE RINDS OF THE SKY
BY BEN CARIGNAN

The Rinds of the Sky

What grand dally the clouds form
And with swift undoing the sun their deposition.

—We must ask:
Is it as difficult for us, as for clouds,

To come and go?

If welkin honey must pour down,
It must ferment while birds and bears drag their hinds.

Thus, on we carry south a soundless wind.

Standing at average height, with decent blood pressure, and born of remote origins, **Ben Carignan** is a lover of the absurd and has a derelict desire for life's lonely miseries. He has been an observer of nature's aleatoric whimsy and continues to observe it as such. In other words, he lives in San Francisco and is otherwise involved in the world brewing beer.

CHILDREN'S &
YOUNG ADULT

Category Winner:
Broken Promises
by Anita Perez-Ferguson

Broken Promises

Chapter 1

"Not too many of those red berries. They will make you sleep forever," Sparrow's mother told her as they collected herbs on a hilltop overlooking the Pacific. "Your grandma called this toyon. People here call them Qwè berries."

Sparrow cared little about picking berries today. She was disturbed to see how enormous her hands looked. When would her body stop growing? Would any boy ever choose to hold her gigantic hands?

"Use three berries for a grieving woman." Mama Nina passed on the family's healing customs. "Never five, or you rest with the ancestors."

"You mean that?" Sparrow pulled back from the bush. "But why would anybody eat so many?"

"In this life, many suffer--defeated warriors, heartbroken widows, and desperate souls. You will understand." The herbs grew in the shade, overlooking the harbor in Monterey, Alta California. Brown pelicans flew in formation on the ocean breezes. "See the birds? They release seeds to grow new plants here. We all have a purpose."

"When will I learn all these things? What is my special purpose?" Sparrow moved clumsily, unaccustomed to the changes taking place in her body. In some ways, she resembled Mama Nina's people, the Chumash, with her dark hair and eyes. "Why do I grow so tall?" Her long legs, enormous feet, and large hands were like Papa's. He was an American.

"You will know your purpose when it is your time. It is our way." Mama Nina bent to gather handfuls of coyote brush. "See this? It is good for skin burns and rash. We also use it for tea." She pushed the brush into her sack. "You grow tall like your papa, Sparrow, not like my people. This is as it should be."

"I may be half-good—the part of me with your Indian blood. But these enormous feet do not fit into my shoes. When Papa comes back, I need new shoes to impress him." Sparrow's slippers were made from her friend's castoffs.

"You need new shoes for new journeys." Mama Nina looked down at Sparrow's feet. "I see you are outgrowing those hand-me-downs."

"He is coming back, right?" Sparrow's papa never visited now that his American family had moved to Monterey. Still, Sparrow knew she would see her papa again, even though the newcomers were disturbing Native ways and tribal people were disappearing from the territory. Mama Nina moved toward the pathway that wound down the hill back to Rancho Duran. It was scattered with wildflowers.

"Look at the poppies, so bright!" Sparrow imagined the flowers in a colorful bouquet. Would Sparrow ever have a beau who plucked blooms for her?

"Poppies are bad medicine. Many beautiful flowers fade away, Sparrow." Mama Nina was practical. The healing blossoms she carried—Qwè berries, coyote brush, sage, and mint—were not so colorful. After Papa abandoned them, Mama started caring for patients using these herbs, so she could in turn, take care of Sparrow.

Chapter 2

Every morning, at sunrise, Sparrow followed Mama Nina to the hilltop to collect herbs and berries or down to the creek to collect water and the small fish caught in their submerged basket traps. Then there were other land traps to check for small animals that they skinned and dried for jerky. Mama's people lived off the land, and now she taught Sparrow all their skills and traditions.

"Here, for our tea." Sparrow collected pieces of honeycomb from a nearby beehive. She loved sweets, and not everything Sparrow ate came from the natural world around her. This was a secret that separated Sparrow from her mama. The two of them lived in a one-room wooden cabin that also served as Mama Nina's herbal clinic. The space was so small that Mama had to roll their sleeping blankets into the corner each morning to make room for her clients.

"Find high, dry spaces between the wooden planks to protect the herbs from the damp air and the mice," Sparrow's mother told her. They each had their morning chores, and then Sparrow and her mother shared hot tea, berries, and little dry cakes made from ground acorns for their morning meal. The cabin could have been cozy, but it was originally a storage shed used to butcher and store prey, so the space smelled of dead deer, bears, and wolves.

"We need more sage bundles to clear the air." The odor of death lingered no matter how many times Mama spread the vapors. Their cabin was on the property of Señor Salvador Tenorio, whose wife, Señora Maria Theresa Duran Tenorio, received regular herbal treatments from Mama. Señora Tenorio allowed Mama Nina and Sparrow to live in the cabin in exchange for her treatments. Sparrow daydreamed about living in the Tenorios' big hacienda.

"They have a perfect life in that big house. I wish we were like them." Sparrow attended school with the Tenorios' daughter, Josefina. Just beyond their small cabin, red clay tiles lead to the hacienda courtyard. The house was built in the shape of a square, with a patio in the middle where flowers grew and little baskets with singing yellow birds hung on overhead beams. Sparrow often saw Josefina's aunt, Alicia, and her sweetheart, Sergeant Valdez, meeting there, and she often imagined the lovebirds' conversations in the shadows.

"Just remember, many beautiful things are fragile," Mama Nina said, waving one more bundle of sage leaves to cleanse the cabin air.

Josefina's parents hosted parties for community leaders in their huge hacienda. Guests included visiting captains, artists, and musicians. Aunt Clara, who also lived in the hacienda, conducted all the family's social arrangements. She knew everyone in town and all about the latest fashions. Sparrow often served refreshments for the guests at these parties. It was on these occasions that Josefina sneaked Sparrow sweet treats from the hacienda's kitchen. Sparrow's mouth watered just to think of sampling the refreshments. The girls sometimes eavesdropped on the partygoers' conversations.

Lately, all the conversations were about the Americans trying to take away territory from Mexico and take power from Governor Alvarado. They wanted the land from San Diego in the south all the way past Fort Ross in the north, where the Russians had already taken land from the Native people. The United States envoys tempted public officials with special benefits described in a proposed treaty named after Guadalupe Hidalgo. If an agreement was not made by 1845, the only alternative was war with the Americans. No one wanted that. With only one year left to decide, the treaty was a subject Sparrow and Josefina studied at the convent school.

"I'll be late for class if I don't leave for school now." Sparrow told a little lie to Mama. She put on the shoes that pinched her feet and hurried off. But she did not go directly to school. Instead, she detoured to the Monterey harbor. Ever since Papa had left to live with his American family, the only place Sparrow was sure to see him was at the docks where he worked. She'd found a perfect hiding place to watch him, but she never let him see her and they never spoke. Just being near him as he tended to the cargo ships made her feel they still experienced something together.

Chapter 3

When Sparrow arrived at the harbor in the early morning hours, the waters in Mexico's Monterey Bay were like glass. The mirrored surface reflected the long-necked shore birds. Seagulls roosted on the sailing masts and squawked their demands for fish entrails and other scraps of food. Larger ships, two and three tiers high, were anchored out in the bay. Each ship flew a colorful flag. Sparrow studied the home port colors of the foreign ships from France, England, and Spain and those of the American ships. Some of their vessels were fitted with portholes for cannons, but these warships were only used for peacetime trade in this Mexican port.

As Sparrow grew, it had become more difficult to hide between the shipping crates. Her hips grazed the packing ropes, and her shoulders were wedged between the boxes. She stayed still and listened for her papa's voice. He worked with other foreign sailors, checking cargo, counting hides, and swapping the news from various ports. Papa knew many of the men from his days working with the American Scientific Expedition. He'd been working for them as a surveyor when he first met Sparrow's mama and became impressed with her knowledge of the lands, rivers, and plants in the Mexican territory. That had been seventeen years ago.

Today, his conversation with the other sailors went on and on. The men's voices were easy to hear because they spoke loudly, bragged often, and boasted about their trapping skills or something they were planning with Papa.

"If your men are prepared, I will show you his routines. Leave it to me." The fellow who spoke had curly black hair and bushy eyebrows, and his voice thundered. He wore some kind of uniform jacket—not Mexican—with a red, white, and blue striped armband. Papa looked around the dock, but Sparrow remained hidden behind the crates.

"If we work together, the governor will soon be out of our way." Then he continued, "Our troops are ready. War is certain, and when we are victorious, this dock will fly the American flag."

Two other sailors with ruddy faces and red beards shook their fists in the air. Their shabby uniforms were faded blue and yellow. Sparrow tried to make sense of their conversation. What were they planning? Governor Alvarado was a friend of the Tenorio family. He had attended many of their parties. Sparrow's hands felt wet and cold.

Out of the way? Those were the words Papa had used. He sounded like he was going to become a traitor. Sparrow squirmed to stay between the packing crates, pressing her lips together to keep herself from calling out, "You can't do that!" Her knees were pressed together, too. She was nervous and needed to relieve herself soon.

Then another man approached—Josefina's father, Salvador Tenorio, who served as the Mexican harbormaster in Monterey.

"Let's keep business moving, men." Salvador Tenorio spoke with an air of authority and interrupted Papa's conversation with the plotting sailors. "Is everything all right here?" Salvador and Papa had known each other long ago, when they were young men. The two men only saw each other on the dock now that Papa had abandoned Mama and Sparrow, and Señora Tenorio had forbidden Papa from coming to the hacienda.

"Yes, sir, good cargo. I've collected the dock fees. You can be on your way now, sailors," Papa said, sending the other men away as if nothing was amiss.

"Stop them. Tell him," Sparrow muttered to herself. How could her papa be making such plans with these men? Was Papa really a spy for the Americans?

When the coast was clear, Sparrow wriggled her body out of her hiding spot, intending to make her way to the convent school. She wrestled with what she'd heard Papa say. If she told Mama, she would have to admit she'd been spying on Papa at the dock. She couldn't tell Josefina, her best friend, because then all the girls at school would soon know. If she reported what she'd overheard to anybody, Papa and his friends would be jailed, maybe even exiled from Alta California. She could never reveal Papa's secret.

Anita Perez Ferguson is an author, trainer, and traveler, who revisits western history and listens to diverse voices to discover a new perspective on her family's struggles and accomplishments in her historic fiction trilogy, *Mission Bells*, about Latinos in the Old West before California statehood. Her books speak to young adults and Latino readers who long to see their own faces and hear their true stories in history. Learn more at AnitaPerezFerguson.com.

Big Rock
by Vicki Montet

Big Rock

He drove his truck right off the end of it!

He was running from the law and should have known where he was going. He's probably the only one who knew these woods that well back then. He rounded that last turn in pitch-black darkness. And then it happened. Earl was never heard from again.

"Are you kidding me? Are you saying that Earl is underneath this giant slab of granite we are sitting on right now?" Sally's eyes were wide as saucers. Her neighbor Billy had told her the story of Big Rock and the man who never made it home. Earl.

Billy and Sally were pals. Every day, the two walked home together from their school at the end of the street. They had to walk right past these woods. Billy helped Sally carry her backpack on the walk sometimes. She had a bad habit of filling it with more stuff than she needed.

She had that backpack with her as they sat on Big Rock. They were deep in the woods, almost a mile from home. This was a time when there weren't a lot of houses in these parts yet. You could walk forever and not see another person or another house. These were dense woods with tall pines that were thick enough to hide behind. It gets dark real fast out here.

When it was time to come home for dinner, Sally's Mom would use this large lead pipe to beat loudly on a horseshoe-shaped metal bell. It's what they used in the old west to call the riders and herders in from the fields. It made an unmistakable metal-on-metal sound- like the worst steel drum you ever heard. Everyone within earshot knew what that sound meant.

Children in this neighborhood roamed far and wide, down to Hodges Lake and up to Big Rock. You could get lost out here. Parents didn't worry so much then. The kids ran free.

"It's starting to get dark, Billy; maybe we should start walking home." Sally was feeling a little uneasy sitting on top of a dead man, and she was a little afraid of the dark.

This was her first time at Big Rock this late in the day, and she knew better than to be out here. "Mom will be mad if she finds out we were out here this late, Billy. We should go."

"Well then, don't tell her, Sally. We can head back in a minute."

Farther down the dirt path toward home, there was a creek they had to cross. Near the creek, some older boys had built a secret underground fort, but everybody knew about it. They literally dug an underground dirt igloo. It was made of Georgia red clay. Then the boys stuck sticks and rocks all inside and around it to hold it up good. Billy and Sally had been told to never go in that underground fort. Ever. But they had to pass it on the way home. Billy brings up Earl again as though Earl might be listening.

"You know that dead man Earl, they say he liked to eat children. He waits until the sun goes down and then snatches them from the woods and hides them underground." Billy was amusing himself now, making Sally squirm. "I don't need to hear all that, Billy. I don't like that!"

Sally stuffed her fingers in both ears and turned away. She stood up and got a little woozy. She didn't realize how high up Big Rock really was. They had climbed up from the lower edge, where it disappeared into the ground. On all fours, they had crab-walked all the way up to the tip of the giant slab of rock. It was about two stories high where she stood. She backed away from the ledge. Down on all fours again, she slowly crab-walked backward down the giant slab of granite, slipping on loose rocks and pine straws. "Come on, Billy! I am not kidding! We need to go!"

The tree frogs were starting to wake up. Their sharp chirps echoed and multiplied across the woods. A few lightning bugs glowed rhythmically in the trees.

Sally had been looking down the whole time as she went backward like a crab on all fours. Slowly she maneuvered the dips in the stone and cracks that broke her slide.

"Billy! Come on!" Almost to the bottom, she stopped and knelt forward on the stone. "Billy?"

Biiiilllllllllyyyyyyy, where are you?!!" She thought he was teasing her at first. But it was too quiet in the woods for it to be funny. Way too quiet. The sun was dipping low now. Barely a sliver of light could be seen poking through the trees.

"Billy?" "This is not funny!!!! If you don't come out, I am leaving you here in the dark!"

Not much of a threat since it was Sally who was now alone in the dark. She ran the story of Earl back through her mind.

He was running from police on a dark summer night. He was a bootlegger, and he had a souped-up car that was designed for wild rides in the woods.

This was a regular run for Earl, and he could lose any policeman in these woods. He hid out here, had a moonshine still out here, and had set traps out here too. Some say that some of those traps still exist. That you could accidentally step on one and be trapped like an animal. And then Earl would show up.

"Ok, Billy, that's it. I am walking home now." She started a brisk walk that broke into a run. She wondered why her mom had not rung the big bell. It was almost dark, and usually that metal sound rattled through the trees right about now.

Sally was mad at Billy. She huffed and puffed his name all the way to the creek. How dare he leave her alone out here. She stopped to catch her breath. The creek was just up ahead.

She pictured Earl bouncing around in his truck, dodging trees and boulders and twists and turns along this path that was once a road. She looked back and knew Big Rock was behind her.

Big Rock used to be twice as big, but half of it broke off and fell on top of Earl and his truck. When Big Rock broke in half that night, Earl was buried alive. So, the story goes.

Big Rock extended out at an angle, and you really could drive a car right up it, even now. But that was a ridiculous thought. Sally didn't want to believe there was a car under there with a dead man in it. She shuddered like a big fever chill had come over her.

Sally didn't have a flashlight with her but felt like she had enough late light to make it home. She stared ahead, mapping the path in her mind. She hears a crush of pine straw underfoot. Then another one, and another one. And it stops.

"Billy? Is that you?" Sally's body was in full fight-or-flight mode. She glanced around, but the fading light made it hard to see. The woods are so thick. She picked up her feet and walked gingerly toward the creek. She stopped. Again, the crush of pine straw underfoot, then another step, and another.

Her hair stood up on the back of her neck. There was a sudden chill in the breeze, and it felt like something brushed up against her. She turned around and around and around again, looking and looking to see what had touched her. There was nothing there.

"Mommmm!!!!!" Sally cried out. "Billllyyyyyyyyyyyy!!!" The footsteps again, but this time sounded closer.

She held tight to her backpack. She knew there was a pocketknife in it, but she didn't want to stop to find it. Sally took off in a full board sprint. She was like a small locomotive plowing up this little dirt path as fast as she could. The gurgle of the creek could be heard up ahead. Once she got there, she would need to leap across the ravine. She had jumped it before.

The underground fort was coming up on her left. She could hear small limbs breaking in that direction, and larger, closer footsteps, like a large man or maybe Bigfoot, she thought. Or worse, Earl!

Red-headed, left-handed, and raised in the south, **Vicki Montet** is an Emmy award-winning Journalist with decades of experience as a TV News writer, producer, and executive. In 2021, she was honored with a lifetime achievement Emmy for that work. She's an Atlanta Writer's Club member, works for CNN, and enjoys wandering the North Carolina mountains and Central American jungles to chase birds with a long-lens camera. Find her at LinkedIn.

BROWNSHEEP
BY JAZZIE DE LEON

Brownsheep

AUTHOR'S NOTE TO READERS: It took five years of sorting through legal documents, personal journals, speaking with available family, researching facts, a DNA test, and my own memory to write this book. No events are composite. I've used pseudonyms for some of the individuals mentioned.

If you're triggered by the deplorable side of human nature, please put this down.

NOTE TO SELF: Your only way out is through. Go. I am waiting on the other side.

Chapter 1

I've heard Filipino referred to as the *ghetto* or *jungle* Asian. I don't entirely disagree. I find it strange that Filipinos are often considered Asian. *Asian* is what I've been instructed to check off on forms requesting ethnicity before *Pacific Islander* popped up as a flavor sometime in the 1990s. I still cringe when I must choose one; neither encompasses the full truth. *Asian* is too large of a blanket term: a one-word amalgam of an enormous continent, its millions of peoples, separate countries, different languages, and distinct historical legacies. The only thing I can compare it to is the catch-all expression *White*, referring to someone of European descent without regard to specific origin—the United Kingdom, Germany, Eastern Georgia, Ireland, even though each region is steeped within their own languages and long-standing traditions. *Pacific Islander* is its own unclear classification which includes the Indian Subcontinent, Southeast Asia, the Far East, and islands in the Pacific Ocean—as if people agreed at some point that we live on a theoretical Pangea.

Some Asians who have caught the public eye are of the elite set. I've seen Singapore or Shanghai types on the silver screen, mainly Chinese or Malaysian, with porcelain skin, educated abroad at premiere universities with claim to monetary resources unknown to common man. The polar opposite also exists in late-night American television commercials: Asians in third-world countries in need of charity that costs less than a cup of coffee per day. Both are valid realities; neither is my own.

My own observations of Filipino culture are that it doesn't outwardly have a clichéd, immediately recognizable, homogeneous history like the Japanese nor traceable royal lineages like Chinese or Koreans. Large Buddhist temples, cherry blossoms, dancers in intricately designed gold costumes, karate, geisha, an automotive line, boy bands, technology, or anything yin-yang hardly has Filipino ties. Even in the lexicon of Asian cuisine—Vietnamese food, Thai food, Chinese food, Japanese food—'Filipino' is hardly a passing consideration amongst those who lunch. I've also heard, in addition to pushing out professional nurses, Navy recruits, and the occasional Miss Universe as national commodities, Filipinos are known for producing some of the best wait staff and house help due to their culture of subservience and eagerness to please.

What the Philippines does have is a long history of colonization, first by the Spanish, then by the United States. My own maternal great-grandparents were both beheaded by Japanese soldiers during the Japanese occupation of the Philippines sometime in the 1940s. According to family legend, during the time when General Yamashita was ordered to concede and pull Japanese troops from the Philippines, the Japanese occupation was so large that pockets of troops either didn't get the message or ignored it and continued to wreak havoc in Filipino provinces. My great-grandparents evacuated their province in La Union, in the northern part of the Philippines, with their two youngest daughters, 11 and 8 years old, into the Cordillera Mountains along with thousands of other Filipinos who unexpectedly ran straight into what they were running away from, Japanese forces who hadn't had their fill of war.

Soldiers massacred thousands, including my great grandfather Diego, who was dropped to his knees at the edge of a river alongside a dozen or more men and women similarly positioned—their heads forced to bow down, the dirty muck of water a sobering last image of this world. Diego was beheaded by sword, head tossed into the running river. His wife, Mauricia, was also beheaded, her head tossed into the river where, I have to imagine, it caught up with my great grandfather's, along with others, in the current.

Of the two daughters, the elder Josefa was apprehended, and soldiers attempted to behead the 11-year-old whose body fell to the ground when the sword sliced through the back of her neck and left shoulder. The eight-year-old, my grandmother Severina, discovered a shallow trench shrouded by fallen foliage from surrounding palm-fig trees, covered herself in dirt and vegetation, and witnessed the entire slaughter of her family. My grandmother passed hours, or days, silent in that pit swathed in dirt until all went quiet. I would hear that she recalled hell-cat noise, rape, the disembowelment of pregnant women, and other heartless acts over the course of the rampage.

The 11-year-old, Josefa, somehow survived despite the massive gash that spanned the back of her neck into her shoulder. When my grandmother witnessed her sister rise from the dead no more than 20 feet away, she sprung from her den towards her remaining family. The two wandered through the tropical mountains for days, Josefa chewing on guava leaves, pasting her wounds with the astringent mush. They ate recognizable plants and were eventually found about 60 to 70 miles south, close to the town of Binmaley, Pangasinan, by a farmer gathering wood. I've been told that as a child, Josefa would later serve as one of the key witnesses during the trial that convicted General Yamashita for the war crimes of his men. My great aunt Josefa would live until her early eighties. Despite the raised scars she bore on her neck and back shoulder for the rest of her life, my aunts and uncles who knew her always spoke of her uplifting temperament, humor, and hearty laugh.

That's one of the family legends about my grandmother and her parents.

There are other variations of how my great-grandmother died. I've also heard that Mauricia fled from soldiers chasing after the beauty with the intent to capture her for sex enslavement in an internment camp. In some versions of the story, she slit her own throat with broken glass moments before capture; in others, she jumped off a cliff, the soldiers but steps behind her. My mother and her six brothers and sisters all continue to tell some version of the three, sometimes forgetting, ignoring, or acknowledging they had told the suicide version before and were now reciting the beheading version. All accounts are still accepted and confirmed by the siblings, even if the stories continue to switch and change in each other's presence.

The three versions were passed down to me, and the only way I can make sense of the disparate accounts is to distill each into a single, palpable message: the Japanese occupation was a violent time in the Philippines, and my family was directly affected. I also had to acknowledge there are even more versions of what happened—the beheading, the throat slitting, the jump, and the truth, which I'd never know, though the beheading version is the one most often told and accepted. Sometimes I find it even more fascinating that the many massacres in the Philippines during WWII have unnerving similarities to the more recognizable Rape of Nanking that's taught in American schools, but like a lot of things Filipino, few know much about it.

In my adult life, with the advancements of DNA analysis and growing genealogy archives, I would spend hours and hours researching this side of my family, confirming relationships, marriages, baptisms, cities, provinces, and dates. I could not, however, verify the bloody details I'd grown up with.

I went searching even further back, going through documents meticulously archived by another culture under the Church of Latter-Day Saints, which holds a large number of Filipino records. Desperate to validate the links of Spanish origin that are evident in all of the names and physical features on both sides of my family, I'd hit a documentation dead end in the 1800s. Spain showed up on the islands during the 1500s. The limitations of records still trigger a childhood irritation of mine of the inability to search and confirm, like a treasure hunt that could never fully materialize.

It was a frustration that haunted and teased me until I realized I was looking in the wrong places. The history is there but not neatly mapped. It's oral. I'd learn to appreciate the oral tradition of the culture as far richer than any written article because the tradition is saturated with color and values that I could never derive from a marriage certificate.

I would also come across a number of scholarly articles about generational trauma, how undefined and hidden nuisances about one's lineage, when passed on to those at an early age, can negatively impact certain people throughout their lives. It's a choice of mine not to abide by those theories, but I can't deny that level of violence has appeared again and again during my own iteration on earth. But even as a child, I had a primal knowing there was *something* I needed to break. I wanted something different. So as far back as I can remember, what I consciously chose to inherit was my ancestor's force of will, the unwavering notion that *survivor* is in my DNA—and it thickens my blood with grit.

Jazzie de Leon is a Filipino-American author and lifelong black sheep. *Brownsheep* is her debut work, placing as a semi-finalist in the memoir category for the BookLife award and finalist here. Critics have hailed de Leon's work as "[a] raw, immaculately written, emotional tale of Filipino immigration, generational trauma, and othering." de Leon lives and works in New Mexico with her partner and two black cats. You can find her on Instagram @JazzieontheJspot.

CHILDREN OF A SECRET WAR
BY MADDY TOROSIAN

Children of a Secret War

Prologue

They should have expected it.

Most already knew. They tried to hide their fear and pain as they always did when men like this came to their door; tried to believe this time was different.

When the procession of uniformed soldiers marched up the only paved street in Arjun, the remaining population appeared; drawn to their doorways and out into the street by the boisterous noise of the soldiers as they passed.

It had barely been three months since the men in the village had been taken, forced from their homes to fight, protecting the empire that already despised them.

This was not the first time. This was not the first village. They should have expected it. The shouts came again. The words in the harsh but familiar tongue announce the unthinkable. In the brief silence that followed, all that could be heard was the rustling of dry leaves in the wiry bushes along the road and the synchronized marching of the soldiers as they made their way further into the village.

Then came the cries.

Women, now widows, sank to the ground as uncontrollable wails echoed from deep inside their bodies. They screamed in the language the soldiers could understand and in the one they could not. But it didn't matter; in either tongue, the grief was translation enough.

A small group of four stood huddled by the side of the road. The youngest, a toddler barely old enough to speak, watched the soldiers from where she stood, half-hidden behind her mother. She wasn't afraid of them—not yet, anyway.

The other woman who had been standing next to the child collapsed at the news as shuddering cries wracked her body. The young girl didn't understand the outburst. She knelt next to her sobbing aunt and gently patted her on the back, chubby toddler hands doing their best to be gentle against the uncontrollable shaking. She whispered soft coos of words repeated from when her mother had soothed her own sadness. When that failed, the child looked up at her mother and tugged at the hem of her skirt, but the standing woman could not move. The child called to her, and the woman's hand trembled almost unnoticeably, but she still did not respond, so the child turned her attention back to her inconsolable aunt.

The fourth member of the little group, a boy, stood next to his sobbing mother, his unmoving aunt, and his young cousin. Unlike the girl, he knew what had happened.

Even at nearly six years old, he understood the place he had been put in. It didn't matter if it was fair or not. It didn't matter if he screamed or cried. He stared up at the procession of men as they marched by. Their leader rode a horse that towered above the child. Eyes met for a brief moment. The boy set his face firm as the man on horseback passed without a word. Once more, a soldier shouted the news to the unfortunate town.

Even after the stunned woman sank to the ground, pulling herself into the arms of her weeping sister-in-law, and even after the young girl was gently taken in as well, soft shaking voices explaining the loss she could not yet fully comprehend: the boy continued to stare after the soldiers. His jaw set tight, refusing to tremble, his eyes tearless.

The soldiers left as suddenly as they had arrived, and all that could be heard were the echoes of grief as they spread like a terrible song through the streets. The town, once again, was left broken and bare.

They should have expected it.

Chapter 1

April 21, 1915

Celine flung open the wooden doors with both hands and stepped into the entry room of the grand house. She padded past the small hallway and through the arched opening. The main room spread out before her with high ceilings and ornately framed doorways. Light streamed past the glass windows of the balcony door, open to allow the breeze from the warm spring day to enter. A plush couch and chairs faced the stone fireplace with a low table between them. Vases and other small trinkets lay on the table, as well as the other shelves and surfaces in the room. Celine slid past the table, careful to not catch her skirt on the corner. She paused, looking back over her shoulder at the young man who stumbled into the room after her. Several wrapped packages balanced precariously in his arms, cloth bags hung at his wrists. The man placed his burden down on the central table in front of the large sofa and then collapsed into one of the cushioned chairs with a deep sigh, his arms loose at his sides as he slouched into the seat.

Celine shook her head at the pathetic display. Her cousin was one of the smartest people she knew, though she would never admit it aloud. That, however, didn't stop him from having a flair for the dramatic.

"Celine? Mihran?" The voice called to them from beyond the open balcony doors.

"It's us!" Celine shouted in response as she sprung forward, hurrying towards the sound. Mihran groaned as he slowly pulled himself out of the chair and followed his cousin.

The salty scent of the ocean filled her lungs as Celine stepped onto the balcony. Ships, large and small, passed through the channel that splashed below the railing.

Gulls called to one another as they surveyed the water. On the far bank, buildings overlapped each other; muted

tans, browns, and blues adorned their exteriors. At the top of the hill, six spires reached tall above the swath of tiled roofs, clustered around a smooth dome with a matching tip of its own.

Wind whipped at strands of her hair and threatened to pull the hat from her head. Celine shoved the brim low against the gust as she strode over to the small table where familiar figures waited. The younger of the two, a fidgety girl, sat facing the river. Her dark hair was pulled back in a sleek braid, the lace of her dress ruffled in the breeze. Her face lit up when she saw Celine, and she opened her mouth to speak, but the other figure at the table beat her to it.

"Celine *jan*! How was your sightseeing?" The older woman asked in the same voice that had summoned Celine to the balcony. Elegantly poised in her seat, the woman turned to fully face her niece. "What do you think of our humble city now that you've seen it for yourself?"

Celine approached the table. "Oh, Aunt Nora, it was amazing!" She exclaimed. "I don't think I've ever seen a place so big before." She tried to keep her voice calm and controlled, as she was told to in school, but the excitement threatened to burst through her chest, and she couldn't keep the grin from growing on her face. "We saw the old city walls, the Hagia Sophia, and the mosque of Sultan Ahmed." Celine gestured to the towers that rose in the distance. "It's incredible: everything is so *old*!"

Aunt Nora let out a bright laugh, that if Celine didn't know her, would have been surprising coming from such a composed woman.

Celine slid into the seat next to her aunt. The table itself was adorned with a platter of dried fruits and a matching bowl heaping with nuts. The other occupant of the table pumped her legs as she chewed on a dried bit of apricot, grinning up at Celine with a full mouth.

Mirhan, who had trudged up behind his cousin, slid into an empty chair helping himself to a handful of nuts from the dish.

"Constantinople is an ancient city, certainly much older than any city in America." The older woman took a sip from her cup, resting it in her hand as she spoke. "Were you able to visit the Grand Bazar?"

"Were we able to visit the Grand Bazar?" Mihran repeated, sarcasm dripping from his voice.

Celine kicked at him under the table while doing her best to keep her attention focused on her aunt. "Of course!" she exclaimed. "There were so many shops I thought I was going to get lost."

Maybe if you *had* gotten lost," Mihran said, cracking a nut against the wooden table, breaking the shell apart, "I would not have had to carry everything you bought back here myself!"

"I seem to remember you happily agreeing to help me carry my things when I told you I would make Kchuch for dinner this week," Celine chided as Mihran pulled the nut from its hard casing and tossed it in his mouth, crunching it loudly.

"Yes, *help*," he retorted through a full mouth, "not indenture myself."

The young girl at the table giggled and Mihran flicked a fragment of shell at her. She brushed it off her dress and stuck her tongue out at him.

Maddy Torosian is a novelist and thrill seeker from New York, where she graduated magna cum laude from the State University of New York Purchase. While at Purchase, her original novel *The Road Home* was chosen to be featured at the 2022 annual Humanities Symposium. When not writing, Maddy can be found training for her next obstacle-course race, adventuring through foreign countries, or climbing any tree, cliff, and building she can get her hands on. Find her on LinkedIn.

PLEASANT AVENUE: SUBURBIA'S HOMEGROWN CRIME SYNDICATE BY CJ MARLOWE

Pleasant Avenue: Suburbia's Homegrown Crime Syndicate

Preface

My name is Domenic Vaccaro, and I founded a criminal enterprise at a time before social media or smartphones; it was comprised of members one would least expect and was located where no one would have thought to look.

This isn't a recantation of the 'good old days' of organized crime, told a thousand times by former members turned informants in the witness protection program. There will be no mention of blood oaths, initiations, or ties to the 'old country.'

We had no 'mother ship' in New York or Los Angeles. In fact, some of those metropolitan areas were where we made a great deal of money, and it was all funneled back to us - in flyover country. We operated far from the prying eyes of authority figures in jurisdictions familiar with prosecuting organized crime cases.

It will be found nowhere in this book that any of us were indoctrinated into a life of crime, and that was all we knew.

We weren't a gang. We had no secret handshakes, tattoos we were required to get, or colors we needed to wear. We didn't drive flashy cars, wear pinky rings, tote guns, or go out of our way to draw attention to ourselves by wearing expensive clothes.

The year 2002 was when all the ingredients were thrown in the pot, and what later culminated lasted until 2011, at a time just before social media, smartphones, and high-resolution security cameras became a staple of society. Text messaging was in its infancy. We couldn't have possibly existed if those technologies were commonplace.

Pleasant Avenue was an ideal combination of socioeconomic circumstances mixed with the perfect blend of motivated individuals, none of whom came from money - we weren't a bunch of privileged brats with too much time on their hands and their parents' credit card in their wallets. Those that were as described were, in fact, our bread and butter.

I did not wake up one morning and decide I would start a criminal enterprise. It was entirely organic. We were successful because we were hidden in plain sight until we eventually became too big, too widespread, to not be noticed.

Those that we called "hangarounds" became associates once a level of trust was established. Associates became captains when they demonstrated they could handle the day-to-day while exhibiting integrity, humility, and, most of all, loyalty. If somebody didn't jibe with what we were about, they were cast out. Many times we could tell right away who was out to prove themselves, fueled by their own ego, and they never lasted long.

Over time, we formulated and executed a wide range of plans of increasing nefariousness for one reason - To make enough money so we all could have a future past high school and into our twenties, the prime of our lives. We justified it by saying it was just like how a high school kid would shovel snow or cut grass for a few extra bucks on the side. We just accomplished this in a more exciting, complex, and profitable manner.

We did not make money to flash it around at nightclubs, impress girls, or buy cars. The majority of the money made went to fund accounts that could only be touched after a certain date. It was meant to be for moving away from home, a down payment for a house, or going to college. Our members bought into this philosophy, and that is what unified us.

Did all that money go to our college funds? Of course not, but the majority did. The rest was re-invested into the organization or paid out in a way that didn't draw attention to us from financial regulators.

We weren't bonded by a blood oath with no way out - People could come and go as they pleased. We were going to take our futures into our own hands and own it rather than go through life wondering why shit kept falling out of the sky on us. That was all our organization was about. Proving the doubters wrong, taking accountability for our own lives, and putting a plan in action that would better our lives in the long run. No one could have predicted the turbulence, challenges, and moral dilemmas I had along the way.

We were Pleasant Avenue.

Season 1: Black Ivy Hat

Early Summer 2002 – The Original Five

Fresh out of school for the year, it was the first day of summer. I was sixteen years old, and my family just moved to a new house that was twice the size of our old one and about thirty miles away. I spent as much time outside as possible. I must have washed my four-wheeler in the driveway as far down as possible so I could be noticed, three times a day.

Was I going to fit in? What are others my age like around here? Will they want to hang out with me, or will I be bullied like I was in my old neighborhood?

Even though my last name is Vaccaro, I don't have a drop of Italian blood in me. I was adopted by a middle-class family of Italian American descent when I was seven years old and never met my biological parents.

I had a sister three years older than me who was my parents' biological daughter and someone I was never really that close with. I was raised with a very large extended family and had a lot of aunts and uncles and so many second and third cousins I couldn't keep track of all their names. The only time I got to see the extended family was when we all gathered on Thanksgiving, where after the local NFL team played, all the cousins would gather for a backyard football game. It was the only time every year when all of us, roughly the same age, were in the same place at once.

It was our tradition.

Once I got to an age where I could understand, I was taught that there were certain members of our extended family I was to be polite to but otherwise steer clear of. That reality was explained to me the day before we moved to South Ketchum.

There was no Thanksgiving get-together the year prior to our move. I never knew if the Thanksgiving get-togethers stopped or if my family simply no longer attended. But I knew that I really missed those backyard football games.

Moving to South Ketchum was an opportunity for me to socially reinvent myself, having moved from an old school where I was bullied severely. In the years to come, I certainly accomplished that, but in a fashion I thought unimaginable in the summer of 2002.

This was a time when the suburban population was exploding. The landscape of South Ketchum was laden with new housing developments, strip malls, and coffee shops as far as the eye could see. Areas that used to be farmland, open fields, and small airplane landing strips meant for crop dusters in eras past were being transformed into to new residential communities. The infrastructure simply couldn't keep up with the suburban expansion. New hospitals, police departments, and fire stations weren't built with the same sense of urgency. Needless to say, emergency services were stretched thin.

We lived in Marlow County, specifically South Ketchum, which shared a border with Athens County to the west. Trinity Village was to our southeast and consisted mainly of older homes with a mix of white and Latino populations. It was a very blue-collar area, as was Marlow County as a whole. To our south was Old Town, which was the commercial center of the metropolitan area otherwise referred to as 'downtown.'

My family lived in Fallon Chase subdivision, which was off a freshly built four-lane road called Pleasant Avenue, a thirty-five mile-an-hour stretch through mostly residential areas that connected Marlow County to Athens County.

The land our subdivision, Fallon Chase, was built on used to be farmland. I heard a rumor the land used to be a mob graveyard, where during the heyday of the Italian mafia, bodies would be buried. I never knew if there was any truth to that.

At this time, our subdivision consisted mainly of vacant lots, some of which had dug-out basements, and most had 'land for sale' signs situated in the middle of the plots. There were a handful of houses that were starting to take their form, wooden 2x4's resembling the partial skeleton of a home-to-be. Our house was one of five that were fully completed at the time.

Being one of the first to move in, I was hopeful that others my age would notice my presence and take the time to introduce themselves to me. I was hopeful I wouldn't be 'drowned out' by the influx of new arrivals yet.

Raised in the Detroit area by a salt-of-the-earth blue-collar family, **CJ Marlowe** is a debut author who has always embraced the underdog role. He currently lives in the southeastern United States, far from where the events of Pleasant Avenue transpired, where he enjoys his career as an electrical engineer. Having played ice hockey at a competitive level for many years, he enjoys attending any hockey game he can find. His other hobbies include traveling to places he has never been before and meeting people of different backgrounds. Find him on YouTube.

Promises
by Mike Jackson

Promises

I hate this part of my job! Thought Chef Ed Madison as he scanned the restaurant's back parking lot, looking for the drunk who was cursing at customers as they parked their cars. He saw a man snoring on the bench by the rack of drying mops. *That's gotta be him.* He shook the man's shoulder, saying, "Buddy, wake up." The drunk snored louder. *Time for a cop call,* Ed figured. Turning to go back into the restaurant, he heard scraping on the pavement. Glancing back, he saw the boozer up and swinging a mop at his head.

Ed stepped back, slipped on a water puddle, and fell, his head striking a dumpster's side. Lights burst behind his eyes. He scrambled up, shaking his head to clear it, facing his attacker. Stepping forward, the drunk raised the mop. A dark shape leaped out from the dumpster's shadow. The chef glimpsed a hat and a long ponytail as it jumped between him and the drunk. Ed saw the drunk swing the mop at the intruder, and his mouth fell open as he witnessed the mop pass cleanly through his rescuer's neck. Ed could see now that it was a man. The drunk swung, again and again, the mop passing through the man with each swing. The chef blinked and shook his head several times. *I can't believe this shit!* Stopping, the boozer shook his head as he looked at the intruder. The dark figure took a step towards the plastered guy. The drunk threw the mop down, turned, and ran through the parking lot and down the frontage road paralleling the freeway.

The chef turned to the figure who saved him. He was a man wearing an old, wide-brimmed hat and a dirty, torn shirt with the sleeves rolled halfway up, buttoned to the neck. I bet he's homeless, but whoever he is, he saved me from my head being split by a mop.

Ed extended his hand. "Thanks, buddy. You saved me from getting hurt." The man shook his hand. The skin felt icy, but the grip was strong. He felt the rough skin of thick calluses.

"You're welcome. I saw you needed help." A smile appeared on the shadowed face.

"What's your name?"

"Jiang."

"Jiang, my name's Ed, and you won't believe this, but when that drunk swung the mop at you, it looked like it went through your body. Crazy, eh? Bad lighting." Ed wrinkled his brow and said, "You're not hurt, are you?"

"No, he missed me with every swing."

Ed noticed the thin face and worn clothes hanging loosely from the man's body. "I can give you a meal. It's the least I can do for your help."

The man scratched his chin. "Yeah, I could use food. Just give me things I can cook myself, like potatoes or beans."

Ed rubbed the back of his neck, thinking, He probably saved me from a trip to the hospital. "Okay, I can do that. Wait here." He went inside the restaurant.

Ten minutes later, he was back with two heavy boxes of food. "I'll help you take it to your car."

"I don't have a… car, you said?" Jiang looked around the parking lot. "There's no train here."

"You know, one of those." The chef pointed at one of the parked vehicles. *Damn, what has this guy been smoking?* "Where do you want to take this?" Ed said. The man didn't answer. "Look, Jiang. Where do you live?"

Jiang pointed up to the mountains behind the restaurant. "I live there."

Nothing there except an abandoned railroad tunnel. He's homeless… probably camped inside it.

"How far?"

"Maybe ten minutes."

"Okay, let's go. You lead." Ed picked up one box, Jiang picked up the other, and they walked up the brush and oak-covered hill.

Ed climbed the brush-covered slope with ease. The difficulty came when he walked beyond the range of the parking lot lights. Stumbling in the darkness, Ed jabbed his knee into a cactus. "Damnit," he shouted. He took out his cell phone, touched the flashlight icon, and a stream of bright light came out. "Jiang, you're leading. You hold this."

Jiang shifted the box to his left shoulder and took the phone. He looked at the front and back and felt all around its shape, especially the bright spot where the light glowed. "I like this," he said and nodded… "very useful." He pointed it ahead.

In a few minutes, they arrived at the tunnel. Ed saw there were no rails, just slight indentations in the dirt where the ties used to be. Concrete covered the edges of the tunnel mouth. Graffiti was everywhere. Ed saw "Zombie" spray-painted on one side and "Resist" on the other. Old tires, beer cans, and ragged clothing littered the ground. "You live here?" he asked Jiang. *What a shithole.*

"For a while."

He followed Jiang into the tunnel, being careful where he stepped. The cell phone light cast jagged shadows as they walked. Water seeped through the cracked concrete, wetting the walls. In some areas, the water formed narrow rivulets to flow to small floor puddles.

Ed took a breath. "It stinks. How do you stand it?"

"You get used to it."

They reached an entryway on the tunnel's right side. Jiang entered, shining the light down for Ed. He looked around at a small room with an old shopping cart laying on its side. The walls glistened with moisture. He put the food down, slipped and barely stopped himself from falling by grabbing the shopping cart. Green slime covered the floor. *This is insane*, he thought.

Jiang put his box down. "Okay, let's go," he said. Ed followed him out of the exit. Two steps into the tunnel, he tripped when his foot hit something solid. On his hands and knees, his nose was inches away from a metal rail. He blinked, shook his head, and looked again at two shiny rails resting on wooden ties leading off into the darkness. There was no trash. The walls were dry, smooth and not cracked.

Jiang sat on a rail, holding the cell phone light in one hand, staring at him. He took a deep breath and said, "We have to talk."

Ed leaned against the tunnel wall, rubbing the back of his neck, looking down and shaking his head. Wiping his hands on his pants legs. *Haven't been drinking today… what can explain this?*

Jiang looked him in the eye and said, "I lied to get you up here. I didn't need your food. The mop passed through my body… I… am… a… ghost."

Ed sat up, breathing deeply, eyes wide open. "You're nuts!" he said. *This guy is either high or out of his mind.* "See you around, pal." The chef stood and walked away. He heard, 'Ed, wait." He paused, heard steps crunching on the dirt, turned, and saw Jiang running up to him.

"Do you believe this?" Jiang backhanded Ed in the face, and his hand passed through Ed's head.

All Ed had felt was an icy chill where the hand passed through from cheek to ear.

Jiang did it again, this time with his other hand, and the same thing happened. He flexed his arm back to do it again. Ed shook his head and held up both hands. "Enough, Godamnit, enough… I believe you," he shouted, his voice echoing in the tunnel.

Ed collapsed to his knees and leaned against the wall, breathing hard and thinking, *Okay, this guy moved hands through my head… it still makes little sense.* "When I shook your hand in the parking lot, you felt solid," he said.

"When I focus hard enough on a body part, it becomes solid enough to move things." Jiang shrugged his shoulders.

They stared at each other. Ed cleared his throat and took several deep breaths, calming a heart he felt beating at high velocity. "Okay, Jiang, you've made a ghost believer out of me. Now, if you don't mind, I've got to get back to the restaurant." He stood up. "I've got a business to run," he blurted.

"Look, I need your help. All I ask is for you to *please* listen to what I have to say so you understand why I brought you here. Afterward, you can decide if you want to stay or go back." said Jiang in a pleading tone.

Ed took another deep breath, rubbed his forehead, and sat down. "Okay, you've got my attention. Shoot."

Jiang gave a half smile. He leaned toward Ed, saying, "I am Chinese, and I was born in the province of Guangdong, China, in 1860. I won't go into a lot of details, but it wasn't good there. So, I went to California... we called it 'Gold Mountain.'" I signed with a labor contractor in Canton and sailed to San Francisco... spent five years grading roads in and around that city.

"Wait. You said you're from China. Okay, I'll buy that. But…"

Mike Jackson is a retired elementary school teacher who lives in Santa Maria, California. He spends much of his time reading, hiking with his dog, Buddy, and gardening with California native plants. He has won a few local writing contests and is attending UCLA's School of Creative Writing, where he finds it very annoying to always be the oldest student in class. His contact email is trailhiker1220@gmail.com.

SUCKER PUNCH
BY ALEXANDRA MULLIN

Sucker Punch

"Are you coming tonight?" Mark was audibly panting on the other end of the call, clanging weights and humming treadmills echoing in the background. Kevin wondered why his friend insisted on making calls while working out but figured that when you're a bonafide social butterfly, you have to multitask.

Kevin was strewn across his living room couch, legs draped over the armrest, aggressively racking his brain for excuses. It wasn't that he didn't want to go out. It was just that he'd rather do almost anything else. Something about small talk with strangers he'd never see again didn't exactly sound like an ideal Friday night.

"You know, I never finished *The Great Gatsby*. Was thinking of doing that this evening." Kevin prayed that his friend had little to no memory of their high school days together.

"Liar," Mark grunted. "I know you read it back in 11th grade when you had a crush on our English teacher."

Crap. Plan B. "And then I have to call my mom..." Kevin felt a ball of anxiety forming in the pit of his stomach.

"You only call her on Thursdays," Mark protested. Kevin could almost hear Mark's smirk through the phone, frustratingly confident in his ability to leave Kevin no choice but to go to this party. Kevin was beginning to question how this man had been his best friend for so long, seeing as this song and dance of social bargaining wasn't exactly uncommon.

Kevin panicked, fearing Mark could tell he was running out of ammo. He was grasping at straws. "...been wanting to try that new restaurant you mentioned. Might order in. You know I have a delicate stomach, so maybe I shouldn't go out -"

"Ok, gross." Mark cut him off. "Plus, it's only open for lunch right now." He clicked his tongue, "I assume that does it? I'll see you at 10. Text you the address."

He hung up before Kevin could protest. Sighing, Kevin ran a hand through his hair, eyeing the French bulldog plopped down on the couch next to him.

"That's right, Bruce. The bad man is making me go out and talk to strangers."

The dog tilted its head quizzically, a string of drool slowly making its way down from its jowls.

"You have it easy." Kevin scratched the dog's ears, "I envy you; you know?"

Tail wagging, the dog yawned and stretched out its paws, blissfully unaware of humanity's plight and wondering only if he'd be lucky enough to get a treat before dinner. Kevin's phone buzzed with a message from Mark.

117 Fairbanks Ave. I'll stick with you.

Within the first five minutes, Kevin had lost Mark to the masses. Sighing, he surveyed the crowd. Kevin debated how long he'd need to stay to say he gave the night a fair chance.

He noticed a woman seated at the bar, seemingly equally uninterested in the event, finishing a crossword on her phone. Kevin made a mental note to work on his own daily puzzle before walking over to her.

"Hey, are you -"

She held her finger up in response, face twisted in concentration. One epiphany later, she'd typed in the missing answer and was turning toward Kevin.

"Sorry about that," She tucked a strand of curly brown hair behind her ear. "I promise I'm only rude when I'm trying to finish the hard ones."

Maybe he'd found a kindred spirit. Kevin smirked. "No problem at all, I can relate."

She flashed him a warm smile, motioning toward the barstool next to her. "You're welcome to join me if you'd like. I'm Michelle."

Kevin wondered what good he'd done in the world recently to warrant this beautiful woman taking an interest in him. Maybe it was that shopping cart he returned or the extra tip he left at the restaurant yesterday. Staring at the seat, he felt a bundle of nerves threatening to engulf him. Kevin gulped and sat down before he could think twice, squashing any semblance of hesitation with sheer willpower and the promise of a little liquid courage.

The conversation was easy, enjoyable even, Kevin noticed. He found himself ready to thank Mark for dragging him out — or at least, made a mental note to be less of a pain about it if Michelle was in attendance. One cocktail turned to four, and suddenly Kevin was disclosing secrets with reckless abandon.

"Ok, hear me out," Kevin announced, unprovoked but with the bravado you'd expect during a Ph.D. defense, "Zumba is the best form of exercise."

Michelle's eyes widened, her face breaking into an impossibly huge grin. "I knew it!"

"So, you agree!" Kevin was beaming. "A little external validation does wonders. I can't wait to tell Mark that he was totally wrong."

"No, no," She waved her hand before adding, "It's not that — I agree, for the record — but I was just struggling to figure out why you looked so familiar."

A horrific realization dawned on Kevin. "You..."

"Teach your Zumba class, yes." Michelle sipped her drink with renewed vigor, fiddling with the umbrella.

"You're a Zumba instructor," Kevin stated flatly, slightly less enthused than his counterpart. "That means you've seen me make a fool of myself for...," He counted on his fingers, "...five weeks in a row now? Wow." He pinched the bridge of his nose. "So, how embarrassed should I be?"

"No joke, you're pretty good," She shrugged. "And it's a side hustle I picked up." Michelle leaned forward, waving the bartender over. "I used to be in a dance company and wanted to find a way to — another Moscow mule, please — get back into that. Capitalism isn't quite as fun as rhythmic dance."

She paused, glancing back at him with a wink, "But I don't need to tell you that."

Kevin bit his lip sheepishly, feeling ever so slightly better given that she hadn't immediately fled upon learning that he was a Zumba fanatic. Maybe they were meant to be, he mused. It was fate. Fate or four vodka cranberries.

Their conversation meandered. Her favorite ice cream was Butter Pecan, which she swore wasn't just for old people. He used to play competitive table tennis and hated the phrase ping pong. She had been getting into karate. He had been thinking of starting piano lessons.

The thunk of a sweaty hand on Kevin's shoulder shook him out of his alcohol-induced stupor. "Hey buddy," the burly figure towered over Kevin, scruffy face difficult to make out in the dim lighting, "I think you're in my seat." He winked at Michelle, who sneered back in return.

Kevin, far too confident in his motor skills given the number of empty cocktail glasses perched next to him, stood up. Even on his tiptoes, he barely cleared the man's chin. Kevin wobbled slightly, the room a bit more topsy-turvy than before.

Time swirled together, the next few minutes a blur as Kevin found himself yelling something along the lines of, "Back off, you oaf!" before taking a swing at the giant — and missing by a mile.

Reaction time somewhat compromised, Kevin barely had time to flinch before he felt the man's meaty fist slamming full speed into his jaw. His body flew backward, whacking into a barstool before he crumpled to the floor. The last thing he saw before slipping out of consciousness was Michelle landing a punch, his oppressor too busy gloating to see it coming.

"You go, girl," Kevin offered weakly before darkness engulfed him. Kevin woke up with chapped lips, a swollen jaw, and the worst hangover he'd ever felt.

"What," he winced, touching his jaw, "What happened?" He was seated on a velvet, gold armchair nestled in the corner of the bar, which had evidently been closed for hours, given the morning light creeping in through closed shades.

Mark emerged from around the corner, an odd mixture of concern and excitement on his face, "Dude, what *didn't* happen?" He was clearly trying to hide a smile. "Bad news: you tried to punch a guy and got absolutely pummeled. But on the bright side, that chick Michelle *totally* got revenge for you. She's got a solid right hook." Mark reached over to Kevin, who was scowling back at him and patting him on the shoulder.

"Michelle," Kevin perked up, "Did she leave?"

"Oh yeah," Mark fished around in his pocket, producing a piece of paper. "I mean, they cleared the place out to clean up. You knocked some stuff off the bar when you fell. But," he handed Kevin a receipt with writing scribbled on the back, "she left you this."

I'll take any punch-related moves out of the choreography for this week.

Kevin groaned, falling backward in his chair.

Mark leaned against the frame, propping his head up with one hand. "You gotta admit, pretty exciting night, though."

Kevin glared up at his best friend before telling the same lie he always did. "I am never going out with you again."

Born in Canada and raised in Dallas, Texas, **Alexandra Mullin** studied Human Biology at Stanford University and received her MBA from the Tuck School of Business at Dartmouth. While her professional life focuses on healthcare innovation, she has always had a passion for creative pursuits such as fiction writing and improv. More of her work can be found at medium.com/@alexmullin, and she can be reached via her LinkedIn page.

THE GREEN GIRL
BY Z.J. MCBEATTIE

The Green Girl

Chapter 1

"Happy Birthday Mizu!" Mizu's mom Kala shouted as the door to Mizu's bedroom slid open.

"Twelve years old!" her father, Biju, yelled, squeezing in behind her mother.

Their smiles were from ear to ear, but their happy expressions did not travel up to their eyes. The creases that appeared shortly after Mizu's older brother Mazu's disappearance five years earlier had deepened day by day leading up to her twelfth birthday. Today, there were bags under their dark green eyes as blue as a stonepad fish, and the normally deep green tint of their skin had turned to a sallow gray.

"A special present for a special girl," her mother said, handing her a box neatly wrapped with precious paper handmade from seaweed.

"Thank you," Mizu said, reaching down for the package from her bed rack and gently setting it on the bed. Her room was tiny, like all the single bedrooms in the tower, with just enough room for a bed rack and a desk and clothes storage below. She sat up cross-legged and tied her short, straight, black hair back away from her face, but a few strands escaped the tie, so she tucked them behind her ears. Thanks to her short stature, her head didn't yet touch the ceiling. She delicately pulled the string that held the paper to the box. Paper like this was special and had to be carefully recycled. G-Aqua-Earth, their home planet, was covered in water, and though seaweed was plentiful, the tower where they lived did not have the facilities or the population to produce goods like this in mass.

"Chocolates!" Mizu cried as she saw the contents of the package. She'd only tried chocolate once, two years ago, when her Uncle Matti, her mother's brother, had brought some back from O-Earth on one of his many trips off planet. Unlike her parents, who were Seals bound to the water, uncle Matti was a Hawk, always flying off on trade adventures to other planets. "A whole box!" She couldn't believe it. When Matti had brought them chocolates before, there was only enough for a small piece for each family member. It had tasted strange at first, and she wasn't sure she liked it, but then the piece had melted on her tongue and the flavor was divine.

This box contained at least five hundred grams, enough to share and savor over time. Then her smile faded, and she looked down at her parents. "But I can't eat this; I'm leaving for training tomorrow." Off-world foods posed a risk of digestive issues, and the rules were very clear about the pre-training diet.

"We know, her mother said. "But we'll put it away, and when you finish the gauntlet, it will be waiting for you." Her mom's voice cracked on the word gauntlet, and she turned her head to brush away a tear before it could fall. "Unless," she added.

Biju put his arm around his wife. "It's her choice, Kala."

The last year had been rough. Until she was seven, there was no question about what path she would take. She was going to be a Seal, just like her parents, and their parents, and so on going back generations. But then Mazu didn't come back. He disappeared during the gauntlet, the final stage in becoming a Seal. So now, instead of the excitement building up to election day that he had, her parents had grown more sullen every day. And as she got closer and closer to her twelfth birthday, they started to point out all the benefits of NOT becoming a Seal. How she could choose to be a Hawk like her Uncle Matti. No one spoke about how disappointed her grandparents had been by Matti's choice. It had become all about "you can fly to different planets." Even worse, she knew they were hoping that she'd choose to be a tower-bound Tiger. Not that there was anything wrong with being a Tiger. The Tigers had far more career and educational choices, and most of her friends would become Tigers. And she wouldn't have to decide between Hawk or Tiger for years to come. Only the choice of Seal required a commitment at twelve, before her body took its adult form.

Every baby born on G-Aqua went through anatomy modifications. Within weeks of birth, an aquabladder was added near the gallbladder in the digestive tract to produce enzymes to help break down the native foods available on the planet. And there were three other surgeries before a baby reached six months. The modifications for Seals were far more substantial and irreversible. But the benefits, at least to Mizu, were priceless. She'd finally be able to swim with the sea creatures without a cage. She wouldn't be bound to the tower. She could go out on long sea voyages hunting or doing research like her parents. And no matter what they might think, the choice was hers. Parents weren't even allowed at the election ceremony. And when she returned from the gauntlet, they wouldn't have to be afraid anymore. They'd see that she, too, was meant to be a Seal. And then maybe they could let go of Mazu just a little and find some happiness again.

"What's going on?" Mizu's seven-year-old brother Mozu asked, pushing past his parents. Without an invitation, he climbed up into the bed rack and sat down next to Mizu. Mizu still found it strange how light his skin color was compared to the rest of the family. It was barely even green, and his eyes were a dark brown. He reminded her of Matti, who spent so much time off-world that he almost looked like some of the pictures she had seen of people back on O-Earth.

Mizu spent enough time in the pools at sea level that her skin and eyes had already taken on a darker green hue than most twelve-year-olds. But not Mozu. Her parents didn't like him to spend time in the water. He would probably end up being a Tiger or a Hawk.

"Moz, it's your sister's twelfth birthday!" Her mom said cheerfully, reaching up and taking his small hand in hers.

"Oh," he said, and his face hardened. He was too small to remember Mazu. Mozu just knew that when he was very small, he had a big brother, and that brother had never returned after election day. And now his sister was twelve.

"Oh, Moz," Mizu swept him up in her arms. "I'll be okay. I've dreamt of being a Seal my whole life, and when I get back, I'll go off on adventures with mom and dad. You'll see, and then maybe you'll want to be a Seal too."

"Absolutely not!" her mother said.

"Sweetie," her father tried to intervene.

"I don't care," her mother said, pushing her father away. "Mizu, we have different plans for Moz."

"I understand," Mizu said. And she did understand. They would have preferred that she stay safe and sound on the tower, but it was already too late by the time that Mazu disappeared. She already had dreams of her own.

Mizu shook her head. It was something she always did when she thought of Mazu. Deep down, she'd never accepted that he had died. When he didn't come back from the gauntlet, she'd become more determined than ever to become a Seal. In her seven-year-old mind, she convinced herself that she was going to find him. She knew better at twelve, but now her quest was to bring her parents back.

"I better get to school."

"You could stay home," her mother offered, trying to make up for her earlier outburst. "We could all spend the day together."

"It's my last day. I want to spend some time with the other twelves before I go off."

"Of course you do," her father supported her. "And you'll be back in six months. It seems like a long time, but it will fly by." As soon as he said it, he knew he shouldn't have. Her mom started tearing up again.

"Very well," her mom half smiled. "We'll have a birthday dinner full of nice risk-free foods tonight."

Mizu climbed down and wrapped her arms around her mother in a big hug. Then she pulled away and looked her straight in the eyes. "In six months, I'll be back, and we'll celebrate my birthday in style and dive into that box of chocolates."

They all nodded and smiled, but Mizu knew what they were all thinking. She was younger, smaller, and weaker than most Seal candidates, and on average, fifteen percent of Seal candidates didn't come back from training, and in the last couple of years, it had been more like twenty percent.

Z.J. McBeattie is a writer, an artist and an engineer. She loves exploring new worlds and possible futures through her writing and hopes her readers will too. These days she lives in San Francisco with her two doggies. She can be reached at zjmcbeattie@ gmail.com.

WAGES OF EMPIRE
BY MICHAEL COOPER

Wages of Empire

Prologue - April 18, 1911

Jerusalem

The Temple Mount was shrouded in darkness. It was the dead of night, yet sounds of digging echoed within the Dome of the Rock.

Gunter von Wertheimer knew the sounds well—the steady scrape of a shovel, the bite of a pick, and the whisper of soil poured from full panniers.

Cloaked in a hooded robe, he stood in the shadow of the shrine and looked up at the sky. Among the bright points of stars, the constellation of the scorpion hovered over the Dome; the sharp stinger formed by a bright star the Arabs called *Lasa'a* poised to strike.

As the digging continued, another sound whispered out of the darkness. "It's time." He knew the voice was that of his friend and fellow archeologist, Rahman B'Shara, a hulking shadow in the darkness.

"You know what you must do," said Gunter.

"It's strange, though," Rahman murmured. "When Walker first came, I thought he was like the others—just another greedy treasure hunter, anxious to get his hands on the golden vessels hidden beneath the Foundation Stone. But once I joined the dig, I couldn't believe how quickly it was progressing."

"Do you still believe he'll break through in the next few days?" "No. He'll break through in the next few hours."

"Because of the spiritualists and clairvoyants he hired?"

"More likely, it's the unchecked access he's had to dig for the last two weeks. Walker also has a keen sense of which Ottoman officials to bribe—starting with the Turkish governor." Rahman turned, stepped past Gunter, and whispered, "There's no time to lose."

"Good luck, my friend."

"Why do I need luck?"

"You know that better than I. His guards are well armed."

Rahman smiled, his white teeth flashing in the starlight. "We have something more powerful than their guns."

"Indeed. We have the power of the Temple."

"In the end, yes, but I was speaking of a power of *this* world—the power of the mob."

"And what a mob!" Gunter agreed. "Thousands of pilgrims in Jerusalem for the Feast of Nebi Musa! When they hear the Temple Mount has been desecrated by treasure hunters, Walker won't need to enter the Temple to experience divine wrath."

"Yes! The faithful will be quick to avenge this outrage." Rahman bolted away, disappearing into the darkness.

Gunter knew he was heading to the Moslem Quarter beyond the northern edge of the sacred precincts. After a few seconds, he heard his voice calling out, echoing among the narrow lanes.

"Sacrilege! The *Frengi* are breaking the foundation stone! Sacrilege!"

Within seconds, two armed Turkish guards with torches shot out of the shrine and sprinted in the direction of Rahman's voice.

Gunter flattened himself against the smooth tiles and watched as they came to a stop, apparently despairing as they heard the words Rahman was shouting.

"Arise to vengeance! The Turks have given over the Holy Mountain to the greed of infidels. Avenge the sacrilege! Arise!"

The guards ran back into the shrine, and within seconds, Gunter heard the anxious voice of Montagu Walker.

"We must get out of here double quick! Hurry! Take whatever you can carry!"

As he waited in the shadows beneath the arches of the arcade, Gunter knew that Rahman had been the one best suited to infiltrate Walker's scheme—to expose and stop him. Walker had hired him as his consulting archaeologist to give his treasure hunt the patina of a legitimate excavation—Rahman, who could trace his ancestry in Jerusalem back for a hundred generations.

Though Gunter was also born in Jerusalem, he was the son of German Templers and never completely trusted by the local population. He was suspected of working for the Germans, the Ottomans, or both.

But Gunter served no colonial empire. He, like Rahman, was a Guardian of the Temple Mount, an order that traced its origins to a time before the holy mountain had a name, a time cloaked in the shadowed silence before history.

A line of flaming torches appeared along the northern border of the Temple enclosure. Shouts of execration filled the air.

Walker and his crew tumbled out of the Dome of the Rock, struggling with heavy sacks, shovels, and picks that scraped and clattered on the paving stones.

"Leave   that   stuff!"   Walker   shouted.   "Run   for   your   lives!" They rushed headlong away from the mob, frantically clawing past one another.

Gunter knew they were making for a gap in the southern border of the enclosure.

The mob surged forward in pursuit, the light of a thousand torches beneath the black sky.

Walker was finished.

The passages and chambers within the Temple Mount would remain sealed, as they had been for a thousand years.

But Gunter knew that others would come—drawn by the power and mystery of Jerusalem. And he also knew that the Guardians of the Temple Mount would be watching, and they would never rest.

Chapter 1- June 11, 1914

Cedar City, Utah

Evan was in no hurry to get home. Finding refuge in a pick-up game of baseball after the last day of senior year, he stood in center field amid patches of parched grass and tufts of saltbush, shirtless in the summer heat of the high desert. The dry ground shimmered beneath the late-afternoon sun, and from somewhere, a chorus of cicadas whined, the sound sustained and rising.

He squinted at the distant contest between pitcher and batter, framed by the rickety wooden backstop and the Pine Valley Mountains. His team was ahead by two runs with two outs in what both teams had agreed would be the last inning.

"C'mon! Get this guy out," Evan said in conversation with himself since no other player was within a hundred feet of him.

Nearly two years had passed since his mother's death, and bereft of her touch, home had become little better than a boarding school with a strict live-in tutor. In addition to the regular high school curriculum, Evan matriculated under the unbending tutelage of his father in ancient Greek and Classical Latin.

He was in no hurry to get home.

Pushing sun-streaked hair out of his eyes, he relished the simplicity of baseball and the camaraderie of his friends—welcome relief from the oppressive loneliness and static mental labors he faced at home. And once the game ended, he wouldn't be going home, but to the dry gulley a quarter mile from the house—there to enjoy the quiet solitude of practicing with his sling.

And tomorrow, graduation...

As a prank, he'd formally requested that his diploma be issued under the name "Pancho Villa." His father hadn't been amused. Nor had he been pleased to discover blank college application forms crammed into a box in the hall closet. Despite Evan's best efforts to the contrary, he had done well enough to gain admission to college. But there was the small matter of the application.

"Let's finish this!" Evan pounded a fist into his worn leather glove and bent at the waist, resting his hands on his knees. He imagined he was in the vast green outfield of the Polo Grounds in upper Manhattan, where he had fallen in love with baseball and with the New York Giants on a hot summer day in 1912, soon after he and his parents had arrived in New York City by steamship, and before leaving by train for Utah. His mother, in the early months of pregnancy, had elected to stay close to the electric fan in their hotel room.

On entering the Polo Grounds, Evan's breath caught—the sweet smell of the freshly mowed grass and the vast sweep of green stretching into the recessed shadows of center field. The majestic glory of the green cathedral was further enhanced by the great pitcher, Christy Mathewson, winning the first game of a doubleheader against the Boston Braves.

His father, not wanting to leave his mother alone all day, insisted they forego the second game of the doubleheader, but Evan's baptismal experience was complete—reborn a new convert to the religion of baseball.

The memory of that day was one Evan cherished—the last time he could remember a sense of easy friendship with his father.

In his imagination, he was now playing center field for the New York Giants against the Boston Braves, with Christy Mathewson pitching. Framed by the huge green stadium on either side, with the first and second decks rising two hundred feet into the sky and filled with spectators, Mathewson stood unmoving—the batter also still but for the bat waving slowly like a cobra, waiting to strike.

"Throw the ball, already," Evan muttered as he picked a stone off the ground and tossed it aside.

Finally, the pitcher reared back and threw.

The batter swung, and Evan heard the sharp click of contact between bat and ball—the white dot arcing upward against the blue sky.

Tracking the ball's flight, Evan uncoiled and began to run, shouting, "I got it!"

Michael Cooper immigrated to Israel in 1966 and lived in Jerusalem during the last year the city was divided between Israel and Jordan. He graduated from Tel Aviv University Medical School and is now a pediatric cardiologist in Northern California, returning frequently to the region for medical missions, serving Palestinian children who lack access to care. His historical fiction is set in the Holy Land; *The Rabbi's Knight* in 1290 - a finalist for the 2014 Chaucer Award for historical fiction, and *Foxes in the Vineyard* set in 1948 and grand prize winner of the 2011 SFWC Indie Publishing Contest. MichaelJCooper.net.

ADULT
NONFICTION

❦

GRAND PRIZE WINNER:
FIRE IN THE MIND – FROM THE BURNING BUSH
TO BURNING MAN, HOW WE IMAGINE FIRE
BY JIM GASPERINI

Fire in the Mind
From the Burning Bush to Burning Man, How We Imagine Fire

"To gaze into a fire is a hypnotized form of observation. This slightly hypnotized condition is surprisingly constant in all who watch a fire ... Less monotonous and less abstract than flowing water, even more quick to grow and to change than the young bird we watch every day in its nest in the bushes, fire suggests the desire to change, to speed up the passage of time, to bring all of life to its conclusion, to its hereafter ... it links the small to the great, the hearth to the volcano, the life of a log to the life of a world. The fascinated individual hears the call of the funeral pyre."

--Gaston Bachelard, *The Psychoanalysis of Fire*

"Hot hot, don't touch!" my mother warned. Four years old, fascinated by the mysterious flicker on the kitchen stove, I ignored her. Fire quickly seared both its appeal and its danger into my earliest lasting memory.

Years later, my father allowed me to add a stick to the fieldstone fireplace in our old farmhouse in upstate New York. His gesture of trust marked a step in my progress toward full membership in my community. Later still, after I helped him rake vibrantly colored autumn leaves into piles, he rewarded me with another milestone in the transition to adulthood: yes, I could strike the match that set the leaves ablaze (we had no awareness of "carbon footprint" at the time. Burning leaves was standard practice.) Though it took a few fumbling tries before I got it right, I felt great pride in my accomplishment. Standing guard afterward, ready with my child-sized rake lest the fire try to escape the bounds we human masters set for it, savoring the complex, spicy aroma of burning maple and catalpa leaves, I inwardly glowed with the awareness of having been entrusted with one of the keys to the kingdom.

My first memory of pondering the question "what is fire?" came a few years later, sitting around a campfire with Boy Scout Troop 43. At that age, I devoted much of my leisure time to tales of intrepid space voyagers who roamed the galaxy, boldly leaped through mysterious time warps, and encountered strange creatures on alien worlds. *What if*, my fourteen-year-old imagination speculated, *fire is actually an alien life form?* Think of it: fires are born, take in food, grow, give off heat, move about when they can, then eventually die—just like living creatures! I can't remember what my fellow Scouts thought of my idea. I thought it brilliant.

That fire might be alive in some sense is not a new idea. The Roman essayist

Plutarch, writing in the first century of the common era, observed that "Nothing bears such a resemblance to an animal as fire." Fire moves and finds its own food, he noted, can die either by forced quenching or natural decay, and when quenched "makes a noise and resists, like an animal dying." From the animist perspective—the oldest human conception of how the world works—everything is alive. The only exceptional thing about fire is how obviously it makes its living status apparent, compared to the subtler lives of wind, rivers, and rocks. Fire can seem to have a capricious mind of its own. Sometimes difficult to light; once lit it can be difficult to put out.

The natural histories of fire and life are deeply intertwined. Most living creatures get energy from cellular respiration. At the core of respiration, a set of processes that releases biochemical energy from nutrients, is a combustion reaction. This form of combustion is a much older sibling to the rapid, harder-to-control form of combustion known as fire.

Of the four traditional elements, fire is by far the youngest. Earth, air, and water existed for four billion years before fire even became possible. Before *us*—we carbon-based life forms—there was no fire of combustion (the forces that heat volcanoes and the sun are very different). Why not? There was nothing to burn.

It took us living things a billion years to create the conditions necessary for our younger sibling, fire, to be born. First, we had to somehow emerge in the seas and produce enormous amounts of oxygen. The atmosphere, which originally contained next to no oxygen, had to contain 13% before the first smoldering fires could occur. How did that happen? We did it, speaking broadly of us living things—specifically anaerobic bacteria, which give off oxygen as a waste product during photosynthesis. Once the atmosphere contained enough oxygen, aerobic (oxygen-needing) creatures could evolve, basing our metabolism on a slow form of controlled combustion within cells. Finally, we had to evolve to the point where we gained a foothold on dry land, then died in sufficient quantities to create fuel from the cell walls we leave behind. Only then did our hotheaded sibling fire have something to consume. Though fire became possible 470 million years ago, during the Middle Ordovician period, the first small, scrubby wetland plants did not offer fire much opportunity. Fire first appears in the fossil record as charcoal 420 million years ago, during the Late Silurian period.

What gives fire its mysterious power? What do we see when we stare, "slightly hypnotized," into our glowing, crackling fires?

Sometimes we see a god - even the God. Those of us who lived near volcanoes saw a *deus ex caldera*, fuming and murmuring when in a good mood but capable of erupting into violent fury. Those who witnessed heavenly fire strike the earth as lightning came to what seemed obvious conclusions about fire gods in the sky. The name of the Hindu god of fire, Agni, derives from an ancient Indo-European term for animate fire that lives on in English in such words as ignite, igneous, and ignition. Over millennia Agni took many forms and wore many faces.

Norse, Mayan, and other cosmologies saw fire as a root force in the universe, older than gods. In other cultures, the powerful, fiery sky god has a friendlier earthly counterpart, the familiar god or goddess of the hearth. The friendly divinities in the kitchen cannot always be trusted, however. They might spy on us, sending reports to the sun about our earthly transgressions.

When not a god itself, fire could still make manifest the divine presence and the divine will. The God of Israel spoke to Moses through a burning bush and led His people through the wilderness with a nightly column of fire. In ancient Greece, after an annual festival at a temple of Dionysus, the god "made a great fire shoot forth" if he intended to produce a good growing season. If no fire appeared, people prepared for the worst. Through the smoke it sends aloft, fire often serves to communicate the other way: we may ask questions through fire, do penance, attempt to appease, or send appeals.

Guilt or innocence can be tested with fire, it once was thought. Immunity to fire marks someone as saint, or shaman. Creatures of fire wander the planet, we tell ourselves: angels and devils; dragons, bulls and horses that breath fire; jinns, creatures of "smokeless fire" born of the hot desert wind much as we are born of clay; a mysterious bird, the phoenix, which after living for centuries sets itself on fire and emerges reborn from its own ashes. Fire serves as an instrument of magic.

For millennia, philosophers, naturalists, and scientists struggled to answer a basic question: what *is* fire, actually? Is it one of four or five "elements" composing the universe? Or is it the *one* universal element out of which all else was born? It seemed obvious that burnable things contained some kind of fire-substance, which escaped when they burned. One early scientist thought he could detect tiny worms of fire. Others thought it consisted of tiny whirlwinds. A famous alchemist published a recipe for distilling the element of fire from urine. (It actually works—for refining the chemical element phosphorus, which spontaneously ignites when exposed to air).

Another line of questions pondered how we humans learned to control fire. Every culture has at least one myth explaining how this happened. Very few stick to realistic stories, such as the one about the ancient Persian king who threw a flint at a snake, missed, but noticed sparks flying when it hit another stone. More often, amazing things had to happen: ancestors brought fire back from a trip to the moon; a fire-child of the sky god fell to earth, was eaten by a series of fish, then captured by a diligent hero; a shaman clasped his wife so tightly that a supernatural being had to rub them back and forth to separate them, creating the first pair of fire-making sticks. In many stories, such as the Greek myth of Prometheus, fire must be stolen from another animal or a god...

Jim Gasperini has had an eclectic career in various creative media, including educational computer games, books about history for young adults, interactive multimedia, and 3D photography. Many of his projects focus on the entertaining presentation of complex information to a general audience. A member of the Board of Directors of the Institute for Historical Study, he currently lives in Berkeley. More about his background and current book project can be found at JimGasperini.com.

CATEGORY WINNER: THREE SECONDS;
BY MELISSA GEISSINGER

Three Seconds;

The view from the northern side of the bridge is spectacular. The untamed wildness of the Pacific sweeps into the Golden Gate and churns against the coastline. Orange sunlight gleams off the windows of the famous skyline, and I almost still believe that this is where dreams come true, that *the streets are paved with gold* like the old-timers used to say.

From here, I can't smell the human shit that stinks up every city block. I can't hear the homeless scream profanities or the junkies beg me for spare change as I try to walk down the street to catch my bus. There is no way of knowing the stress that families making $150k a year are under, unable to afford groceries, or one unexpected illness away from bankruptcy.

I creep forward beyond the shelter of the Marin Headlands, and an angry, resentful wind replaces the calmness. I instinctively zip my jacket tighter to shield my neck from the frigid gusts, though I'm not sure why it matters.

A fleet of tourists rushes by on their rented bicycles. More than ten million people every year pass under these golden towers woven tightly together with coiled cables. What draws them to this particular bridge, I wonder? Is it the fact that they initially said it couldn't be built? That these waters were too dangerous to attempt any architectural feet such as this? Was it that this golden-orange primer, declared offensive and ugly by so many, was never planned to be its actual ending hue? I marvel, knowing only eleven men lost their lives during its four-year construction. Yet, this timeless landmark, the epitome of strength amongst turbulence, this bridge that joins worlds, this testament to human fortitude, is about to become the stage for my self-annihilation.

I walk. I touch the cold, orange guardrails and hope to absorb somehow the stories of others who have taken this same walk. The unseen thousands who have been in this same headspace. The silent sufferers. The hopeless. The broken. The unfortunate souls on the receiving end when God either felt spiteful or just plain didn't give a fuck.

These rails hold memories. They remember the thousands of sad people looking for the perfect spot to end it all, the over seventeen hundred who succeeded, and the countless others who walked away.

Finally, I approach the midpoint of the bridge. Both towers reach above me with their Art Deco arms and reassure me with their grandeur.

"This is a safe place," they tell me. "Soon, you'll disappear."

Three seconds. I keep playing this over in my head. I don't remember where I had heard it, but somewhere they said you have just three seconds to jump. If you don't do it within that

time, either you'll chicken out, or someone will stop you. I don't think anything can change that much in three seconds. I'm entirely unconvinced that any of those things would happen. I couldn't possibly pull out at this point. I had come this far, after all. And I am too cynical to believe that anyone would even notice me, let alone care enough to try to save my life.

Regardless, I decide I will jump on the count of three. It seems poetic, anyway—a solid plan.

I walk further and find what looks to be the perfect spot. I can easily climb over without any barrier in my way and plunge into the concrete sea. I take a peek over the edge so as not to raise suspicion, and I feel a wave of fear thunder through my veins and ricochet off my skeleton. Okay, I admit it. It's a lot scarier now that I'm here.

My back pocket buzzes, and I don't even need to look at it to remember why I'm here. I take it out and wind up to throw it off the edge, but my curiosity gets the better of me, and I unlock it. It's her.

At my mom's. The kids are fine. Don't follow me.

"Oh, but I will be following you," I say as I chuck the device into the waters below. "Be right there, darling."

A middle-aged couple walking toward me arm-in-arm sees me and stops. The husband looks like he's about to say something but pulls his wife's arm in closer, and they continue, making a wide pass around me.

I hover at my chosen spot and wait a minute for them to vanish. I grip the square railing and squeeze. I feel the golden paint peeling under my fingertips. "Not as perfect up close, are you, old girl?" I whisper.

Cars rumble by at impossible speeds and shake the bridge giving it a palpable pulse. They all have places to be, but not me. The only way I'm going is down. The world around me becomes a blur. I focus only on the infinite expanse beyond the steel.

Fuck. Here we go.

One.

I place my left foot on the bottom of the railing and swing my right leg up and over.

My wife left me, and for good reason. My mother is the only one who loves me, and she's terminal—two weeks to live.

I hate myself. I'm an awful husband and a terrible father. I am not enough. I'll never be enough. I'm a fuckup. I'm cursed. Everyone who gets close to me suffers.

Two.

I bring my left leg up and hoist my body to sit on the railing.

My future is below me now. I'm scared and so alone. I have nothing: no money, no career, no partner, no home, no future. I wanted to be a pilot. To soar above the clouds and be free. Hold my head high as I walk through the terminal, demanding the respect of everyone who sees me. But that's not how life turned out, did it? Instead, I got fired from a job where I cleaned up shit and piss for a living. I'm a complete and utter failure. What the fuck happened? Where did everything go so wrong?

Three.

I look left and right. I feel the anguish in my heart rise up, and I'm surprised to find myself desperate for someone to notice me. *Please, goddamnit.* Someone, anyone, look up from your phone and see my face. Can't you tell I'm in pain? Can't you tell that all I need is someone to care for *one second*? I'll tell you everything. I'll unload a dump truck of emotions on you. The pain needs a conduit, a place to go—but there's nothing. No connection. No pathway. It's an open circuit.

I lean my body forward and let go.

Four.

The wind is so powerful I feel as if I might take flight. But this is not freedom. This is not salvation. No! This is unjustifiable extinction.

I take it back. I changed my mind. I want to hug my mom. I love my kids. They need their father. I want to tell my wife I'm sorry. *I want to live!*

I turn my body so my feet will hit first. Please, God, let me live;

A neurodivergent optimist, **Melissa Geissinger** is predisposed to following her dreams as well as every side quest along the way. It's nothing short of a miracle that she's been able to finish her first historical fiction novel, *Nothing Left But Dust*, coming April 2023. Proud mama to a 5-year-old heart warrior who, like her, is driven by curiosity, she injects adventure into their lives at every opportunity. She's a content designer at H&R Block, a fire survivor, and a serial entrepreneur who enjoys wandering the wilderness with a camera whenever "lifey stuff" gets too overwhelming. You can follow her writing, both UX and creative, at melissageissinger.com or on Instagram @ melissageissinger.

DESTINATION: ACCEPTANCE
BY SHANA MCLEAN MOORE

Destination: Acceptance

Silly me. I keep thinking I have reached acceptance of my mom's mortality like it is a physical place I can arrive to and decide to stay. Build it a picket fence and a flourishing garden with a deep-rooted tree to symbolize its permanence.

In my head, it sounds a little like this royal decree I pronounce to myself:

"Well, you *thought* you had reached acceptance when she lost interest in her favorite treats, but now that she eats just a few bites per day, you officially come to terms with the truth that she doesn't have much time left. You accept this because you don't want her to suffer anymore."

Isn't that *adorable*? Even I don't believe it.

I call for a care-team meeting and sit down with three wonderful women who have gathered to discuss how my mom is doing.

"She is so happy much of the time, Shana," one of them offers.

"I know, I love to see her dance and sort of entertain the troops like she's on her own little USO tour," I say. "But I'm concerned about her weight loss. By my records, she has lost nine pounds in the first three weeks of June."

"Oh yes, I'm not surprised. She really doesn't eat much lately," she adds.

"Listen, this *is* my first rodeo, and I have no idea how hospice works, but if you think she's a candidate, I'd love to get her as much support as possible."

I say this so stoically that it feels like a would-you-prefer-paper-or-plastic situation at the grocery store. *Who am I?*

"Well, we do refer to hospice when our residents start to eat a lot less and sleep a lot more, so I think it's appropriate to have that conversation with her doctor now," she says, validating my suspicions.

We go to the doctor the next day, and Mom is her engaging self. The recent symptoms of aphasia make many of her words unintelligible or nonsensical, but her energy conveys good cheer and positive energy.

This is the blessing I encounter daily during my visits: Her life is stripped of home, her dog, her independence, much of her dignity... and yet she is quick to laugh, eager to dance, and sings along like a little Hallmark caroler figurine lip-synching lyrics just off enough to be believable.

How can Mom be admitted into hospice while still able to entertain and be entertained?

The duality of her condition leaves me routinely sucker-punched.

I get the call from hospice. They will be coming to assess her from 3:00-3:30 the next day. What I assume is that there will be some questions and the taking of vitals, and then a call back with their determination. What happens instead is that the nurse arrives and stays for two and a half hours, presenting me with a Welcome to Hospice binder and many forms to fill out.

Do I check the box that says she can be intubated? Get IV fluids? Comfort only? Would she like visits from a chaplain?

Then, there is the question that shatters like a cheap-ass-dollar-store-glass the denial that still remains: Which funeral home would you like to use?

I asked for this assessment, and yet… I am not at all prepared for their decision to be so quick and obvious.

Shortly after, we have our moment. Mom and I are snuggled up on her twin bed, looking into each other's eyes and expressing how lucky we are to be loved by one another. And then she utters the statement that makes me hold my breath: "I want to see my parents, and they want to see me."

Mom becomes preoccupied with her parents for weeks. She also says vague things that make me feel like we are talking about her death, but I find myself tiptoeing away from acceptance yet again by saying, well, maybe she's saying she wants to be *free* of all the helpers who guide her throughout the day, not *free* in the sense of transitioning to eternal life.

There's a lot of talk about "going." One day she says, "The people were trying to help me cross over." Another time, while joyfully dancing in her chair, she proclaims, "Shana, I'm so excited to move on. To go from here to over there." But the most jarring is when I tuck her in for a nap one day, and she declares, "I think I'll walk in the forest instead."

Listen, this is the same girl who trained me to fear nature down to the suburban shrub, and the only place she was ever spotted walking was down the aisles of TJ Maxx. As I process the shock of her choice to make like Little Red Riding Hood, she follows up with a quick, "Do you have weapons?" *No, Ma, I most certainly do not.* I drive home, certain that this little metaphor means she is telling me she is dying soon.

And then, of course, there are two weeks of no mention of anything otherworldly. I make another declaration that will likely sound cute by the very next day: "From here forward, I will do the day in front of me and not try to read into what all of this might mean."

Much of my struggle with trying to anticipate her end of life comes from my deep desire to be by her side, telling her, one last time, that she is the best mother, wife, sister, daughter, grandmother, and friend a person could ever hope for as she moves into the afterlife. It is a "place" I haven't exactly believed in until now when I need to, making me one of those dreaded bandwagoner "fans" who hop on the hype when the local team makes the finals.

I hope it is a destination like I want acceptance to be... where we can meet amid the lush gardens in the shade of the deeply rooted trees.

Wearing her heart on her keyboard, **Shana McLean Moore** expresses the nuances of joy and pain in being a daughter, mother, wife, friend, and embarrassingly late-blooming feminist. When not working on her memoir, she helps her coaching clients build balance and satisfaction into their busy days and provides daily loving care for her parents as a thank-you for a lifetime of emotional riches. Her joys include the beach on a blue-sky day, playful pats on the ass, dining al fresco, yoga breathing, tri-colored sunsets, cuddly pups, and any time her people can gather. ShanaMcLeanMoore.com.

LIFE REVISITED
BY MARIA BARRS

Life Revisited

Life Revisited is a memoir in development that, much like the life it examines, has hit some rough patches. In the interest of preserving relationships, it has been pulled from the anthology at the writer's request. We wish the author peace and wisdom as she navigates this difficult terrain. And that she will continue to write with the vivid realness and ruthless self-examination that caught our judge's attention.

Maria Barrs is one of thirteen children—first girl, three older brothers—a birth order she believes shaped her essence by age eight. A girl's gotta be a bit pugnacious to get along in that environment. At fifteen, amid the chaos of fourteen people living in a mobile home, she dropped out of school and ran away. Homelessness quickly grew old. She earned a GED, graduated college, married, raised two children, and worked in television news, eventually becoming a news director and general manager before deciding that what she really wanted to do is write mysteries. Her first will be published in the Fall of 2023. MariaLynnBarrs.com

LOOKING FOR MYSELF SOBER
BY MARY STEPHENS

Looking for Myself Sober

My Last Drink(s)

Sunday, August 7, 2011

Half-asleep with my robe and glasses on, I padded down the hall in a trance-like state toward the promise of coffee, trying to ignore the cement mixer churning in my head. As I turned right into the kitchen, the morning sun peeking over the hill seared my eyeballs; I reached blindly to lower the shade to half-mast and open the bay window because there didn't seem to be enough air in the room. Sliding aside an empty wine bottle on the kitchen counter to make room for my coffee preparation, I caught an unwelcome waft of sticky sweet chardonnay. *Note to self: you didn't need to open that second bottle last night.* I'd have to remember to get it out to recycling before Nate noticed. On autopilot, I pulled out the canister of ground beans, put a paper filter in the coffee maker, added two scoops of coffee grounds, then water.

While the coffee brewed, I peeked into the family room to see the kids playing intently: Connor with his wooden train track and Brooke with the Legos. I took advantage of a few more minutes of alone time, downing a couple of Advil and pouring myself a cup of coffee. I added a splash of French Vanilla Coffeemate and then another because it was that kind of day already. I gave it a stir and a sip and prayed it would quiet my headache.

I took my coffee and sat on the step leading from the kitchen to the family room.

"Good morning, guys."

"Hi Mama!" they replied in unison, Brooke rushing over in her pink pajama short set to give me a hug.

"What are we doing today?" asked Connor.

"Oh, we are going to have so much fun. We're going to my friends Barb and Roger's house for lunch, and they have a swimming pool."

"But *we* have a swimming pool," Connor whined. "How far away do they live?"

Brooke joined in. "I just want to be with *you* today, Mommy!"

I rested my forehead on my knees. I did not have the energy.

"Oh, come on now, guys. It'll be fun!" I nudged Brooke off of me and retreated to the kitchen. As I topped off my cup, I noticed my post-it on the cookbook stand: "Make bloodies!" *Right! I'd told Barb I'd bring Bloody Marys today.* That perked me up; a little day drinking would cure what ailed me. She and Roger were big foodies, so I wanted to make them really sizzle. Years ago, I'd won a Bloody Mary contest at a college football tailgate party, and I'd been bragging about it ever since, so my friends requested them on a regular basis.

I pulled down a pitcher and started adding the ingredients: tomato juice, Worcestershire sauce, Tabasco, horseradish, and celery salt. While most rookies would stop here, I was just getting started. My Bloodies had ten ingredients. I'd gotten the recipe from a bartender in San Francisco when I was slurping them down like water, trying to drown a hangover. I cajoled the "secret" recipe out of her and jotted it down on a cocktail napkin. It got blurred with Bloody Mary stains, so when recreating it, I just rummaged through the kitchen and added whatever sounded good 'til I reached the magic number ten.

Next in: balsamic vinegar, olive juice, lemon juice, and A-1 Steak Sauce. And today, the tenth ingredient would be ... I opened the fridge for inspiration ... dill pickle juice! I had to chill the drink to give it a taste test, and as I pulled out the freezer drawer, I saw the frosted blue and white bottle of Grey Goose nestled in the ice. So tempting. I couldn't resist getting the party started so I pulled it out along with a handful of ice. I poured, I stirred, I sipped ... ahh, the vodka's warm glow jump-started my engine. It was a taste sensation.

Concerned that Nate would frown on me for drinking in the morning, I poured one for him, too, and brought it down the hallway to the office.

"Hi hon – just doing a taste test on my Bloody Marys. Let me know if you think it needs anything."

He was at the computer, his usual roost in the morning, and absent-mindedly accepted it, giving me a slight side-eye as he placed it on the desk without taking a sip.

On my way back to the kitchen, and to my drink, I glanced into the family room and saw the kids still miraculously playing nicely. I'd been so preoccupied with my mixology their existence startled me for a second. Their little heads with wispy brown hair were bent over a joint Lego project now, so I tiptoed past them, got my drink, and headed to the shower to get ready for the party.

I was excited to see Barb and Roger and their new weekend home in the wine country. I'll never forget meeting Barb about ten years ago, when I was 36, at a hot restaurant called *The Last Supper Club* in San Francisco's gritty Mission district. I was readjusting to single life after my train wreck of a first marriage ended (one-year, bad choice, more on that later), and my friend Stephanie was an enthusiastic accomplice. We were both television producers and got invited to many of the same events, such as restaurant and hotel openings. Steph invited two friends to join us for dinner, Barb and Karen, who turned out to be a ton of fun. We were four single women out for a fabulous night, just like in *Sex and the City*, sparkling in the glitter of city life. We drank four bottles of Prosecco before even glancing at the menu, and a friendship was born. The rest of the evening was a fun, glossy blur, ending in a blackout for me. I could only remember a couple of snippets of the later portion of the night: being jostled in a dark, crowded bar and then sitting on some random guy's kitchen counter while he made us quesadillas. I was annoyed at myself the next morning for losing my favorite black leather motorcycle jacket somewhere along the way and chalking up another one to the casualties of a fun night.

The sound of Brooke coming down the hall, crying, brought me back to the present.

"Mommy, Connor knocked down my Lego tower!"

Six years later and I was a housewife in the 'burbs. How did I get here? Brooke pressed up against my leg as I blow-dried my hair, her little arms wrapping around the top of my thigh.

Don't get me wrong – it's everything I'd always wanted – but I was still adjusting to the huge lifestyle change. I'd quit my job a year earlier because I was jealous of the nanny's gig, but it was like entering the witness protection program. I had a brand-new identity as a suburban housewife. It was still hard to wrap my head around it, voluntarily living outside the city, and raising two young kids at home while my husband worked. After my first marriage ended when I was 36, I was afraid I'd lost my window to find a husband in time to have kids and that I'd be one of those single-in-the-city career women for life. I had my routine down, solid career (writing/producing HGTV shows at that time), a strong group of friends I met up with nearly nightly, and a nice (but lonely) rental apartment in San Francisco. But just before I turned 39, I met Nate. He was tall, dark, and Jewish -- just my type -- and he was the answer to my manhunt prayers: good-hearted, warm, funny, handsome, intelligent, and sensitive (karmic payback for husband #1). We married just before I turned 40. Six weeks later, I was pregnant, and we bought a house in the 'burbs of Marin County. Connor was born just before our first anniversary, and Brooke followed twelve months and eighteen days later. When they turned three and four – old enough to be at preschool a few hours a day (I was no dummy) – I decided to hang up my producer's hat and stay home with them because I was just so in love with them. And it was awesome. Sometimes. It was so cute to see their excitement when I picked them up at preschool or surprised them with treats, but it was also mentally and physically exhausting being a full-time parent. I had no idea.

So today, I was more than a little hungry for some good ole Barb and Mary fun. Desperate for it, in fact. While we were loading the car, I said to Nate as casually as I could muster, "I won't overdo it, but I'd like to have a few drinks today, so would you mind driving home?"

Mary Stephens has written and produced for HGTV, Food Network, and National Geographic on everything from killing Hitler to choosing pillows. While her life appeared picture-perfect, Mary secretly battled an addiction to alcohol. In her upcoming memoir, *Looking for Myself Sober*, she lays bare her messy struggles of early recovery while navigating life as a sober wife, mom, and friend. Mary is currently an MFA candidate in creative nonfiction at Dominican University of California and lives in Northern California with her family. Email maryrosenthal@gmail.com.

My Mom Is My Biggest Enemy
by Shreya Kelly

My Mom Is My Biggest Enemy

What if your mother is so obsessed about your grades to the point that she stops seeing you as a human being? I could never get her the grades she wanted from me, and she never gave up. She wouldn't kill me. She wouldn't let me live either. She was constantly watching me like a hawk and displayed hyper behaviors all through my life with her. How does it feel to be stuck in an enemy country where your enemy soldiers are restlessly searching for your hideout? Imagine having to live like this every day. You are hypervigilant all the time. Your body is trying to protect you from your own MOTHER. You won't have any freedom. Your every action should please your mom for your survival. A regular mother defends her child when the child is accused by others. My mother not only falsely accused me, but she wasn't even believing me when I was trying to justify. Yes, my mom is my biggest enemy. I have Complex PTSD, Borderline Personality Disorder, and Peter Pan syndrome because of her.

An outside person wouldn't even be able to stand mom even for an hour. They will be able to sense that mom is toxic. Unfortunately, I grew up with her. I didn't even know that I was being subjected to torture. I grew up thinking that all mothers are just like her. So, how do I heal? I can heal only if I destroy all the foundations that are deep-rooted in my brain.

I will narrate a few incidents to describe my switch in thinking:

1) I was cooking noodles at night while preparing for an exam. She ran into the kitchen and yelled, "you are wasting time on food to escape studying." She doesn't empathize that hunger is a primal instinct for human beings.

2) Not only did she want to see me with books every day, but she also wanted to control my study timings. I wanted to study till midnight one day. She wanted me to wake up early the next day and study. I locked myself in my room as I wanted to study. She banged on the door while being abusive. I still didn't open the door. She then turned off the electricity mains so that the light in my room turns off. She has no self-control. She does anything she can to hurt me.

3) When she didn't find some money in my wallet, she automatically assumed that spent it on watching a movie. She wasn't trusting me when I told that I bought

two ice creams. She was so insecure about my grades to the point that she wasn't even trusting me. She used abusive language for half hour. She further screamed that she unnecessarily paid my school fee. She suddenly changed her tone of voice. She switched her tone to a sweet voice from a screaming voice to ask, "which movie did you go to?" She was hell-bent to prove that I watched a movie. So, she decided to do manipulative dramas (by changing her tone). I firmly stuck with my ice cream story. Then she again switched back to the screaming voice and threatened me, "I will go to the store and check the cost." No parent behaves this way with their 17-year-old daughter. They will be more concerned about their daughter's feelings over proving that she didn't study. Mom finally got convinced that I ate ice creams after she verified the cost of ice creams. She never apologized for her behavior. She just lets her insecurity rule her life to the point that she is always out of control. Not only was she insecure if I wasn't physically in front of books, but she was also insecure when she imagined that I wasn't studying. Her stupid imaginations are always untrue. I didn't watch any movie.

4) She won't let me do anything else other than studying. That includes not letting me text. One night, when I took a few minutes longer to go to my room from the bathroom, she suspected that I was going to take my cell phone from the living room into my room. She was guarding me from her room (while remaining awake). She screamed and ran towards my room. I quickly took my phone, ran towards my room, and bolted the door before she caught me. Can you imagine a more controlling mother?

5) If you think this is bad, what about having a mother who also wants to control your thoughts (not just your actions)? When I told her about my favorite movie actor's daughter, she screamed, "those people are trying to feed their bellies by acting in movies, and you are wasting time for them." She doesn't hesitate to be disrespectful to your face just because she wanted you to THINK only about studies all the time. It is possible for any human being to not think about anything else? When I relayed a conversation with my friend, she demanded, "how do you know this?". I told "my friend told." Then she screamed, "do you girls just waste time in school in meaningless conversations?" I told, "it was lunch break." Then she said, "your heart knows what is true and what is not." She never trusts me. She is that insecure about my grades.

6) Though I studied all the time, whenever her colleagues told her stories about their kids, she came home and demand why I was not just like them. She just feels insecure at the very thought that some other child could be 'better' than me. When I told her that I was not getting enough time to finish the syllabus, she did not believe me. She demanded, "then how does PQR get enough time?". Why is it mandatory for me to be the most intelligent person? Why can't any other child do better than me? Why couldn't she empathize that her daughter might not be the most intelligent person? Just because some other child is 'better' than me, why does she not trust me?

7) When I informed DEF's mother that she visited my home (in attempt to keep her with me longer), her mother yelled at her (over the phone) about being underdressed. She cried after hanging up. As soon as she cried, mom felt insecure about her parenting. Mom manipulatively gaslighted me for half hour. She repeatedly said that other kids are afraid of their moms, and I was not. In reality, I was more afraid of her than others. She just refuses to believe it with her madness fueled by her insecurity. She picked on me for calling and informing her mom (like it was so wrong). She brought up a petty fight with DEF (a few days ago) and yelled, "you girls fought a few days ago, and suddenly, why is she your best friend?" Why was she manipulatively gaslighting me? What was her stupid motive? Was she trying to imitate DEF's mom? She further screamed that I was not observant of the situation I was in (it seems our grandfather was sick, and they were thinking of taking him to the hospital). I had no idea about that. She wouldn't stop. She continues till her insecurity wanes out. How is creating chaos the same as imitating DEF's mom? None of that would have happened if DEF didn't cry. DEF is that type of a person who cries for everything. Her mom is much better than my mom. She is very respectable, loving, caring, and empathetic.

8) The two human needs are: being able to do what they like and being able to converse with the person they are living with. Can you imagine not being able to do anything you like and not even being able to converse with your mother? She wouldn't believe me. She cut me in the middle of my conversations and bullied me (while giving threatening looks). Just because she was so unhappy with my grades, she didn't have the right to torture me every time she saw my face.

I did not know how to react when I was being subjected to torture and disrespect. When you have problems, you tell your mother. What will you do when your mother is the main source of your problem? I grew up in a very unsafe and unpredictable environment. Strict parents are not unpredictable parents. They just have more rules. The kids know the rules and the consequences for not following them. They still grow up in a predictable environment. I didn't even know what to do with my mother in such an unpredictable environment. I was stuck in a solution-less problem as I couldn't get those grades. I couldn't stand up for myself as she was making things worse. My emotions never got regulated, and I have constant racing thoughts. I just remained frozen for several years.

Shreya Kelly was traumatized by her own psychopathic, hyper-angry, and narcissistic mother who had unreasonable expectations of her. She is the only one in this entire world who has autism, BPD, PTSD, Peter Pan Syndrome, anxiety, and depression. She started healing at 29 and wants to help other trauma victims heal faster (with her blogs). You can read more about her here: https://vocal.media/beat/i-was-breastfed-by-a-psycho.

THE AUDITION
BY RIKI CARIGNAN

The Audition

My thumb brushed against the luxurious cognac leather of my bag. I thought of the foreclosure notice. The giant gray house on the hill I longed to leave, but with nowhere else to go. The heavy bag pushed on my legs, my dry eyes flickering, intermittent like the canopy of fluorescent lights above me. At twenty-nine, I was in my second year of music school, a childhood dream in the making since I was eight. I was different from my new friends at the university, not only older, not only a single mother but also an immigrant struggling with the English language. The doors in the back of the room squealed as I clutched my bag, watching the blood drain from my knuckles.

Inside my bag was the brood of things I carried in an unremitting juggling act, sheet music for the clarinet concerto, and a financial aid application. I opened my Day Runner where color-coded schedules for the children lined the pages. A diagonal hurried message from the Los Angeles Times reporter who was chasing my story, and a yellow sticky note with the familiar handwriting that made me beam: *good luck, I love you!*

The waiting room of the Los Angeles County Office was crowded. It reeked of sweat and soiled diapers; a whiff of harsh cleaning solution hit my nostrils with a pungent sensation. A baby cried in the corner, begging for comfort. WELFARE FRAUD IS A CRIME, read a poster on the wall, pictures of the villains were printed in little black and white squares. One of the photos resembled the man who threatened the roof over our heads to punish my children for my senseless desires.

Small children wandered aimlessly, their imagination not yet tainted, unaware of the dire existence of their mothers. They did not know what it was like to stay up half the night worrying if there was enough cereal in the box for breakfast, or the taste of regret for believing the older man from America who promised the freedom of financial security. Grimy crumbs of Oreo cookies, a crimpled Skittles candy wrapper, a half-chewed pencil, my eyes traced and re-traced them on the gum-stained beat-up colorless carpet to escape the dread in the faces around me. The American dream seemed to have skipped this room. But my dream, the one I hung onto since I was a little girl in a small immigrant town in Israel, that dream was still alive, burning inside of me.

A white plastic clock hung on the wall, ticking time away, a prisoner of the seconds, hours, days. I heard myself sigh. I wanted to believe it was just temporary for me, a bridge to my music degree. I kept hearing my mother's voice in my head. *Music is not good profession for wife and mother. You must sacrifice, for the yeladim.*

Was the judge going to think I did not sacrifice enough for my children? I placed the back of my hand on my forehead, feeling the pulsating sensation of my head; my eyes struggled to stay open. The dullness around me matched the despair I felt, and my mind cycled the events that brought me to this place. An unforgiving whisper nagged. *I told you so.* Was it my mother's voice or my own?

I sat upright, rolling my shoulders, watching a boy play in the corner waiving a small car, his mouth blowing motor-like sounds, roaring into the apathetic room. I smiled at his innocence, so much like the cheerfulness that resided in my children's eyes. His mother sat on a wobbly chair, my eyes crossed with hers, a momentary connection. Shame made my ears hot. I fidgeted, rubbing my numb feet against each other, my right hand reaching for the flutter in my chest. I shifted in my seat, the heavy bag nearly falling off, when I heard a voice call my number.

"Two thirty-nine!"

The woman with the voice stood in front of a tiny office, holding the door, her eyes scanning me from head to toe, arched eyebrows lifting when she paused on my bag. I swallowed the dryness in my throat, my shrinking courage melted into the sweat of my palms. I handed her my forms and sat facing her for an awkward beat while she snapped the pages neatly filled out with my artsy handwriting onto a deteriorating brown clipboard.

"How can I help?" Her voice husky, direct.

The words I practiced with Gavin the night before got scrambled in my head.

"Is this your bag?" Her voice came in strong, like a declaration.

"Why... yes, this is my bag," I sounded more irritated than I'd wanted, like an imposter caught in the act. My face heated up; I felt the familiar red rash breaking on my neck.

"It looks expensive is all." She was relentless, but she was not wrong. I almost laughed at the absurdity of it all.

I wrapped my arms around the bag, wishing to erase it from her memory. I dug up the words about asking for help, and I mumbled my request, surprised that I could sound so feeble.

"I'm here to request temporary assistance... three children..." I cleared my throat, too embarrassed to continue.

I knew she was unmoved, and I knew she was not going to help me, and maybe she couldn't, but I answered her questions, my voice robotic, lacking passion.

"Twenty-nine... came to the United States ten years ago... three... nine, seven, four... music school..." The last two words faded into the stale air.

Music is not good profession for a mother... The woman's face contorted as if hearing my mother's voice in my head.

"You own properties?" The question I feared sliced the air with a high pitch, and my shoulders shuddered.

"Mm... Not exactly... I mean, legally speaking, yes. But he does, and I don't have..." She pushed her chair and stood on her feet. Her lips were moving, but all I could hear was the ringing in my ears.

My hands shaking, I made my way out through the screechy doors. I looked over the earthquake-ravaged street to see if I was being followed to my car. I heard my shoes press on the torrid asphalt, the oppressive heat reminiscent of my hometown in Israel, where my love affair with music began.

～ ～ ～

Saharan dust settles on Or-Akiva, the weary people of the small coastal town are anxious for the Mediterranean wind to carry it, and their *tsarot,* elsewhere. On summer days, the blazing hot sun is covered by haze, the humid air suffocates, with no refuge from the unabated heat.

The town has one main street, no traffic lights, a post office, two grocers, four synagogues, a modest library of donated books, two grade schools, no high school. After eighth grade, boys go to vocational school to become welders or plumbers. If you are a girl, there is no real need for education, and you can choose one of these boys to marry and build a kosher home in Israel. You will have lots of male children under the watchful eyes of old women who sit on the bench at twilight, fanning themselves with a piece of cardboard and occasionally spitting to keep away *a'yin ha'rah,* the evil eye.

My mother doesn't approve of the packs of children that flood the streets. They are up to "no good," she says, as she triple-checks the locks on our flimsy front door. Most other parents work in the nearby cannery, but my father teaches in one of the local grade schools, while my mother stays home with my sister, brother, and me.

In a small corner kitchen, she cooks and bakes meal after meal. Fragrant coconut-chocolate cake brings gentle comfort while my parents fight into the night, alternating name-calling in Arabic, Hebrew, and French. My father slams a door, I breathe sugary cinnamon and the intense aroma of cumin, and I hear angry clanking of pots and pans like a stubborn North African beat. Love and hate of my Moroccan culture dance inside of me, pulling me apart, shame and pride living side by side. Mahbuba, our neighbor who lives on the other side of the paper-thin wall of our duplex, hears everything and uses it as a reminder that my father's education doesn't make us better. She hisses at me in mockery when I come home carrying my maroon clarinet case, as if western classical music is a communicable disease.

I am sixteen, music is my place of serenity. It is also my only ticket out of this impoverished and provincial life. In the doorless room I share with my younger siblings, I practice my clarinet for the audition in the big city of Tel Aviv, knowing my neighbor hears everything.

Whether writing, painting digital art, or singing metal music, **Riki Carignan** is always seeking an outlet. Raised in the strict Moroccan Jewish culture in Israel, she views the arts as a pathway to finding her unbridled self. At age 19, she immigrated to the United States and later attended music school, where she met her husband and songwriting partner. As a talent agent, she represented TV/film composers, and as a vocalist, she fronted the band Season of the Crow. A Californian at heart, she loves her family, cooking, reading, photography, and movies. Find Riki on Instagram @ rikicarignan.

THE SECRET-TELLERS' MASK
BY WREN JENSON

The Secret-Tellers' Mask

I'm moping under a table, disembodied legs surrounding me like I'm in a fleshy forest. I ignore the nurse trying to coax me out. She says, "Just smile. It'll help you feel better."

I hiss, feral and cornered. "I can't smile away abuse." She just stares.

So, I close my eyes and leisurely rock. This always works.

Her shrug carries her back to the nurses' station. From behind the counter, the staff all watch us; we psychiatrically ill patients. They feel sorry for us, and they don't want us to escape this hospital and kill ourselves under their supervision. When we leave, our life is ours; until then, we slop down food, meds, and therapy—mostly willingly. Why don't they realize they watch that impossible lock on the door and their matching keys more than we do?

I bang my head on a table leg quiet enough for the nurses to pretend they didn't hear and claw my thigh with short fingernails. Grippy socks all around me slowly scrape their chairs away. I want to nip at these sock-covered ankles, but they know I'm under here to escape flashbacks and body memories, and one morning they might be under here, and I don't really want my ankle bitten.

Or maybe I just feel sorry for them too.

Some patients only need to stay a few days; we seasoned Crazies stay weeks to months, and our bleach-faded socks go from forest to something akin to vomited broccoli—kind of like the dried vomit I saw at a previous psych unit from a patient who was wrestled into the padded room.

Nurses screamed, "Oh my god! She's trying to hang herself with her pants!" and rushed in there.

She seemed fine the next morning.

A few months ago, I played card games with a psych tech, Card Guy, in that vomit-covered hospital. While looking at his drawn card, he said, "There's a look about the ones like you." I cracked a joke about how he has a terrible marriage, which made him laugh because he knew he had a terrible marriage, but he wasn't locked in a psych unit.

He gave me a high-five when I left a few days later. Ten days after that, I walked back onto his floor stripped of everything but a hospital gown, and he said, "I knew you'd be back." That time when I left, he snuck his pack of cards onto my side table.

Now, though, I am at one of the few complex PTSD and dissociative identity disorder (DID) hospitals pockmarked across the country. On the verge of another suicide attempt one night, I had thrown sweatpants with ripped-out drawstrings and t-shirts in a bag. I jumped in my car and drove eleven hours and begged them at two in the morning to lock me away. They did, because they saw I belonged in this place, a broken child in an adult body begging for a place to just *be*.

It's been a while, maybe Card Guy thinks I'm dead.

Another patient shuffles under my table.

I freeze but blink, then freeze again.

She squishes herself against the opposite table legs, our grippy-socked feet almost touching. There's that inch gap of air between our bodies that indicates to the nurses that we aren't going to suddenly pummel each other with the flexible, "bendy" pens and adult coloring books they let us have. Or jump into madly passionate lovemaking, shuddering the tables in an embarrassing display of Batshit, Nutcase, Crazy.

All we did was give each other a tentative smile, the smallest but most terrifying invitation to stay. We loosened our shoulders. She looked down at the ankles surrounding us and hid a smile behind her pink and blue hair, but I saw, and I think she knows that I saw. I smile.

A couple of days later, I am shut in a room that is already locked in a psych unit. My inpatient therapist sits across from me. I've been talking—with words, I think. Or has it just been strangled noises?

Whether or not I speak out loud, I still hear words inside. They blend with scattered, sudden pictures.

Hooded cloaks.

Full moon.

Secrets.

Buried.

Your fault.

I just need to breathe more deeply than those horrors give space in my chest for so I change topics.

But I still tell her of death. I tell her about when I was seven years old and found a suffering robin. Maybe it was a wing? I thought it might be hungry. Maybe my cat tried to gift it to me but only half-succeeded in this sacrificial ritual? Back then, I didn't know that robins don't eat honey. I didn't know it was dangerous for them, but I couldn't claw worms out—what was normally mud was cracking dirt under brown grass. My parents laughed when I showed them the bird, so I found a small, spaghetti sauce-stained container and flopped the robin in with hands too small to be gentle. I put honey in a delicate dish in the corner of the robin's new nest.

I sat with it for hours.

Then it died.

I buried it, digging the dirt with a stick long past the time my shoulders sunburned.

I gave a eulogy to this mound of dirt.

"Dear Robin. I'm sorry I couldn't save you. I'm sorry if I killed you. I didn't mean to. I wish you could've flown away from Abinidi (that's my cat who probably killed you). I should've kept him away from you, but I didn't know that I needed to, and I'm sorry about that. I still really like my cat. I hope that's okay. But your name is Robin because no one should die without a name. The end. Goodbye."

Neither of us cried after Robin heard those lost words. One, because Robin was dead and dead things don't cry—sometimes dying things even stop mid-cry. A silencing so sudden that it strips truth from their throats and lies from the heart of any witnesses.

I didn't cry because I'd seen death.

I also didn't cry when the next morning, there was a haphazardly dug hole in place of Robin's grave, and she was gone to a place I would never know.

I felt a kinship with Robin, and that night in my dreams I thrashed underground in a box, alive and surrounded by dead bodies mottled and fresh alike.

In the middle of my first-week inpatient, I find out that the other patient who thought about nipping ankles with me is named Gemma. She is sitting with another patient, a guy, who looks at her chest.

He says, "Hey, Gemma, I have a question. Are your boobs real?"

I look at him, eyes wide. Do I need to say something to defend this Gemma woman?

He sees me and says, "What? I'm gay, so I can ask that."

I don't know the rules of being gay because if I ask, then someone might ask in return if I'm queer of some sort, and I can't say yes, and I can't say no, and I hate silence.

Gemma gives a polite answer about her transition and hormone therapy when she was nineteen and the guy launches into his history with trans friends and because she can save herself I just sit there feeling anxious that I have nothing to do.

Later that day, I misgender Gemma. Not because I don't view her as who she is, or because I forget, or because it isn't obvious she is a woman. It is because I am ignorant. I blame it on a derisive religion. I blame it on society. I blame it on having too many pronouns in my own head, but really it is just my fault, and I blubber and make excuses, and she smiles graciously like she has never heard anyone misgender her.

I think our potential alliance is over, but she seems to forget my sin and I'm intrigued with this woman who wears large bows and mermaid-print dresses, so I forgive myself.

I feel like a wraith later when I wander into the courtyard. Brick walls replace white walls, but at least the sky is free.

I walk twenty paces, brush the brick with my fingertips, twenty paces back, brush the brick with my fingertips. A cadence with my feet; a caress with my hand.

I think about how we are those macabre, morose characters who crouch in twisted hallways because open rooms don't have enough exits or shadows.

We experience evil not as what we would perpetuate but as our courage to step away from the ledge, the end, that intoxication of fatality. Nothingness shrouds stars, laughter, dance, tears, dreams, hope. And what of music? Wraiths only hear requiems, and there is a time when we wonder if we have already heard our own.

It's the juxtaposition of true evil violating our young innocence that produces the fractures we hold ourselves together with, wraith-like.

Wren Jenson (they/them) is a satanic ritual abuse survivor and dissociative identity disorder (DID) system. After their suicide attempt, they became a passionate advocate for mental health research and innovative treatments. Currently, they are a graduate student at King's College London studying both psychology and neuroscience in mental health with the intent to focus on psychedelic research for DID and C-PTSD, benefiting fellow childhood abuse survivors. When they are not giddily entrenched in school, they enjoy writing poetry, playing with AFAB non-binary fashion, collecting visual art, and instructing trauma-informed yoga. Follow them on Instagram: @ velvet_in_october and learn more at VelvetInOctober.com.

Trouble Ahead:
Dangerous Missions with Desperate People
by Susan Burgess-Lent

Trouble Ahead: Dangerous Missions with Desperate People

Monday 26 May 2008 Kutum, North Darfur, Sudan

I'm up early, preparing for the trip deep into the northern rural areas where the schools are situated. Though there are over forty schools, we'll be visiting only six. Fortunately, I have little insight into the dangerous nature of this mission, though I get a bit twitchy when the GOAL field coordinator shakes his head upon learning our destinations.

We comb cramped little shops for bottled water and treats for the kids, then set off in late morning along a ridge line that leaves us visible for miles.

Every road in Darfur is a back road – clay with ruinous potholes, seasonally passable if you don't mind serial, gut-wrenching jolts. The entourage is ever-changing during the long day's journey. The two constants are my translator Eldooma, a wiry, thirty-something man with watchful eyes, and our driver Ibrahim, a wisecracking specialist of the sidelong glance. A stocky, dark-skinned man with close-cropped hair, Ibrahim is outfitted in a khaki suit. His major asset is an ancient Toyota four-wheel drive with an open back that carries both people and assorted bundles.

Over a rise, we spot several trucks bristling with armed men. My first thought (clearly heat-addled): how will this obstacle mess up the schedule? We approach slowly. I see a shoulder-mounted grenade launcher and an AK 47 toted by two fierce-looking guys, faces wrapped in black kufiyas.

Eldooma jumps out of the truck and approaches them. Then suddenly, an eruption of hand-slapping greetings and loud laughter. As it happens, they are his former students. An arrangement is explained: their group will shadow us to ensure our safety. I pray an armed guard will not provoke an attack from unseen mercenaries prowling the path ahead. We continue on. Heat and noxious fumes from the engine rise from a hole directly beneath my feet.

At one point, we approach a clearing among sparse trees, a small village of burned-out huts. I ask to stop to take a few photos. Though wishing to accommodate me, the men clearly are ill at ease. The scorched, earthen foundations once anchored the shelters of families. A shroud of sorrow seems to hover over the place, perhaps the spirits of those murdered or driven out. It is a dead space, and we leave, spooked and silent.

We rattle across brittle sandstone ledges, traveling in a general northwesterly direction. One must live here to know where villages are. The schools cannot be found on any of the maps I carry.

Our first stop is Abdulshakor Primary School, where eighteen harried-looking teachers endeavor to educate seven hundred and seventy-six children. The kids cheer and laugh loudly, jostling for a look at a freakish, pale-faced, white-haired stranger in the midst of an entourage of Sudanese young men.

Prior to the genocide, the village of Abdulshakor had built a primary school with three permanent buildings and several temporary structures. When the killing began, the school was destroyed. Abdulshakor residents re-established the school in a new location. These classrooms are only marginally useful during the rainy season because the roofing is not waterproof.

Their water well is located about four kilometers away, necessitating a donkey to haul goatskin bags of water several times a day to the school. The children eagerly scoop and slurp grey water with dirty hands and ancient tin cups. I imagine the pathogens gaining hosts.

We head west to Forug School, one of the oldest schools in the Kutum locality. The teachers stress the need for textbooks, notebooks, pencils, blackboards, and chalk. Many of the kids display a reassuring exuberance, mysteriously undiminished by the destitution that surrounds them.

We are off again to a third school. A pair of mangy dogs paces the truck, entertaining themselves during a dull afternoon. I watch a hobbled young camel attempting escape from a group of huts. The heat ripples off the desert as we make our way on shifting, nearly invisible tracks to Shobani School.

In 1996, Arab militia attacked and completely destroyed Shobani village. The residents returned and rebuilt. Eight years later, a second attack over two days left eighteen people dead and the homes in ruin. The current Shobani School opened in 2005, but as with all Darfur schools, the government has remained indifferent. They don't have textbooks. Computers are entirely a fantasy. They must dig pit latrines.

After visiting four schools, I realize we have not eaten, though I've been guzzling water all day. The sun finally shows signs of closing down its fierce torture. It occurs to me, with no small rattle of anxiety, that we cannot navigate a return trip in the dark. It's pitch black when we arrive at the village of Ain Sero, a rebel stronghold hidden in the crusty hills northwest of Kutum. I'm beyond tired, probably hyperthermic, and bereft of any ability to be cordial.

Our contingent enters an area lit by a cooking fire amid huts. A slender, pretty woman in a green tobe greets us, gently taking me into her care. Her toddler lurches from a hidden space, gets one look at me, and cuts loose a terrified howl. I imagine he's never seen a white person, certainly not one looking as disheveled as I must have. Fortunately, his mother finds his reaction a bit amusing and quiets him. She brings me a pan of water and a bar of pink soap that seemed never to have been used. After I wash the dust from my face and hands, she sets out a cot with a heavy woven blanket.

I cannot imagine needing it, but as it turns out, nights in the high desert get pretty nippy. I gratefully lie down. She brings me a warm Pepsi. It's all so unexpected, so hospitable.

I listen to the crackle of the fires where the men have gathered, talking quietly with each other in Arabic or their tribal language; I cannot be sure. The aroma of roasting meat soon mingles with the scent of wood smoke. I watch the shadow of my hostess as she prepares a meal, wondering if she knew that she'd have visitors tonight and if we are a burden of mouths to feed. My stomach denies any interest in food.

Someone arrives and speaks quietly with her, making her laugh – a sweet high riff like notes from a flute. I want fervently for nobody to ever take that simple joy from her. Her baby boy, now bedded down on a cot beside me, sleeps peacefully. I lay peering up at a banquet of stars, denser and more luminous than I have ever seen. A donkey brays loudly. Two camels take up call-and-response bellows. Firelight dances over the dark faces of the men. I surrender to the understanding that I have never been farther from everything familiar. No one I love has a clue where I am. Yet, in this remote distressed place, gentle people are willing to keep a stranger alive and safe. The miracle humbles me.

A young man quietly kneels beside me. "Sister," he says. "Phone." It seems impossible, but Suliman's voice, from thousands of miles and another civilization away, asks in his best casual tone, "How are you?" A satellite phone and a solicitous boss will find you anywhere.

At first light, Ibrahim cheerfully bundles us into his truck. On another featureless road in the vicious morning sun, the vehicle quits. I do not panic, as anyone sane might rightfully have done, given the impossibility that the disabled truck would be found by an adequately equipped passerby, or worse, that we might be set upon by roving militia.

Ibrahim's expression reflects nothing beyond mild irritation. He lifts the hood and tinkers around while the rest of us huddle in the narrow plank of shade beside the vehicle. I do not see what he is doing, but soon he hoists himself behind the wheel. A few cranks of the starter and the engine sputters to life. We will not die today in this particular patch of hellish isolation.

Around the curve of a rocky hillside, we come upon a copse of palm trees arrayed around a spring. An oasis! It's my first experience of the mythical haven for weary travelers. We pile out of the truck, smiling and laughing as we wash our faces and hands in the cool water. A young man wanders off, returning with an armful of mangos. We feast on the sweet fruit, our energy refreshed for the rest of the dusty trip 'home.'

Safely back in my humble accommodations, I rest, grateful for a bit of solitude. Slipping off this edge of the world, I discovered a new way of seeing humanity. I know that if life in my own neighborhood ever descended into the anarchy that defines the lives of Darfuris, though we imagine it never could, I'd absolutely want them in my corner.

Susan Burgess-Lent is a veteran international aid worker, warrior for women's rights, author, and public speaker. Her published works include two novels, *In the Border-lands,* and *When All the Girls Stopped Singing* (publication pending), the rest of this non-fiction book *Trouble Ahead: Dangerous Mission with Desperate People* (2019), and numerous short stories and essays. SusanBurgessLent.com

WAS. NOT WAS.
BY MARSHA M. EVANS

Was. Not Was.

It wasn't dark. It wasn't damp. It wasn't scary. There were windows and light. There was a Nico-blue hydrangea as old as me, large enough to make a fort at the base with my books and my candy. There was a big sandbox in the back, a swing set that would tilt if you got things swinging too high. There was a lawn in the back and a patio where you could sit in the sun on woven-seat folding chairs with white, blue, green, and sometimes yellow stripes. The kind that would pinch the holy hell out of your fingers if you weren't careful.

It wasn't dank. The air wasn't heavy with foreboding. People came over, and they laughed, they played cards, and had a drink. There were dinner parties with round tables and royal blue or forest green tablecloths that fell to the floor where we could bring a flashlight and be safe during thunderstorms. There were pale blue candles that rolled down like ram horns as they burned and were fascinating to touch and to lick.

It wasn't loud. It wasn't angry. It wasn't hateful. There was a neighborhood. A nice middle-class neighborhood with children our age, and you could run up and down the street shouting and playing. Your neighbors' houses were your houses, and your house was their house. Wherever we were, there we were. We had no fear of the inside or the outside. We learned to ride bikes and to avoid potholes. We walked three blocks to school by ourselves from kindergarten to graduation.

It wasn't stale. It wasn't looming. It wasn't ripe with the scent of perversion. There were rose bushes and pansies and petunias. There were hanging baskets full of hot pink fuschia, hot blue lobelia, and sweet alyssum. In the spring, summer, and fall, there were open windows and soft breezes. In the winter, there was ice to crack on standing water by the road.

It wasn't unkempt. It wasn't forlorn. It wasn't loveless. The mid-century modern living room was always kept clean and fresh. Spotless but comfortable. Welcoming to friends and family, kids and adults, dogs and cats. It was inviting and loving and giving to those who arrived for a meal or a drink or a chat. We learned to put our things away, we learned to be conscious of our environment. We learned to be house-proud. We learned how to grow up to be adults, and we learned to respect the adults in our lives. We learned we were special, but we also learned we were not.

It wasn't desolate. It wasn't scarce. It did not seethe with anger. Holidays, Thanksgiving, Christmas, were full of relatives and joy. Golden, golden light. A sparkly tree, smells of cinnamon and cloves, smells of turkey and pumpkin pie. Presents shopped for with thought and care, wrapped in beautiful and interesting paper with spiral ribbon on top. Special outfits for Christmas Eve and new dresses, gloves, and hats for Easter. Laughter and fun and candy canes almost as tall as we were. Easter baskets hidden throughout the house, and Easter eggs hidden throughout the yard. Being lifted from the ground and tossed into the air.

It was not dead. It was not lifeless. It was a home full of movement, of action, of play, and of learning. It was a home we felt safe to return to. It was a home that breathed in and out with our lives, where crying was soothed and where laughing was joined. It was full of color and texture, inviting exploration and feeding interests. It was a home of its time, cultured and warm. We went to museums, we walked Point Defiance, we had barbeques on a 50-year-old grill made with rocks and a slab of metal – driving there with Gus in the back of the 1920s Tally-Ho on property that was meant for our house later on. We saw the Music Man, we sang the Sound of Music, we danced the ballet, the tap, the spinning free-form childish modern. We dressed up for Easter, for the Mother-Daughter Tea, for birthday parties, and for the honor of eating at a restaurant. We were introduced to color and pre-school and travel to handmade toys and homemade clothes and elegant adults.

It was a place where the things that could happen in the night didn't linger in the light of the morn. Yet one does not negate the other – now or then.

Marsha M. Evans is the product of a culture where women are expected to keep a smile on their faces and a secret in their hearts. Having spent her life with friends telling her how they saw her as so happy and full of life, she decided to write an essay-based out-pouring of all she's been through and who she is behind the mask. The result is *Self Harm*, a memoir of sorts digging into her most vulnerable, most hidden, and most shameful parts - an "…I will make you hurt" project, if you will. She is an accountant by day but dreams of being so much more.

WHERE THE LAND MEETS THE SEA
BY DIANA NADEAU

Where the Land Meets the Sea

Acknowledgment

I wish to acknowledge the Abenaquis, Wabanaki, and Pennacook people of Maine and New Hampshire, the beautiful and precious land where I grew up. My love and honor of that land has kept me alive all these years, and I wish to express my gratitude for the care and honor these tribal people offered to that land pre-colonialization.

As well to the Chelamela, Siuslaw, Winefelly, and Kalapuya people of the beautiful Willamette Valley region of Oregon, where this book was written I wish to express my gratitude for their deep connection and care, acknowledge their lives, and name their loss.

I wish also to acknowledge the Coast Salish and Lhaq'temish people of the sacred Washington coastal regions. For I was so touched by the spirit of the shores where they lived that the inspiration for this memoir was born, born upon their sacred land.

Diana Nadeau, on April 10, 2021

Part One: The Sea

Boundaries

The shadow of a white, puffy cloud darkened my world as it covered the sun. Its passage gave a momentary respite from the hot, humid day, a respite I did not ask for or need. Summer is my time, and I love the heat of it.

Nevertheless, I was entranced by the outline cast in the sand from the cloud. I pondered the feeling of cool shade and gazed across the waves to where ocean and blue sky kissed, blushing upon the horizon. The contrast of sun and shade left room for possibilities, such as light sparkling off the waves in the same instance that I sat under a darkened canopy. The scent of ocean drifted by and pulled on my attention. The North Atlantic is distinct, strong, and salty, its depth and power sensed only by those who know it. I breathed until its smell took hold within my memory.

As faraway beachcombers meandered, their tanned bodies brightly lit in the afternoon sun, I noticed the edge of that cloud's shadow moving toward me. I wanted to touch it. I wanted to grasp the point of distinction between sun and shade. I reached out, but the cloud passed. As I and my direct world became awash in June sunlight again, distinctions were forgotten, but an understanding within the exchange of light and shadow lingered.

My shoulders absorbed the heat while the returning sun made the ocean and all things seem less distant. Waves rolled to shore in a rhythmic, tumbling melody of sand and sea. My shoulders tugged on a deep, happy breath; not a gleeful happy that might overtake a giddy toddler, but rather a joy that one feels when knowingness settles in.

Half of my butt rested naked in the sand as my hand-me-down bathing suit rumpled beneath me. It was gritty, but it didn't register as anything other than normal; it didn't occur to my two-year-old mind that one could actually sit at the beach and not get sand in their crack. I dug my toes in deep, feeling cool, wet sand beneath. A warm and dry top layer cascaded around my ankles in contrast. I heard my mother call to me from somewhere behind. I didn't as much ignore my mother's calling as I did continue to lend my attention to the moment; her voice, her very existence, couldn't match the draw of the sea. With its song and surge, the sea commanded a power over me like a grand and all-loving mother over her child, more so than my own mother. And so it was that I remained on my sandy butt for what seemed like the entirety of my childhood but was really only a brief moment in the life of a toddler.

My mother beckoned again. As a growl in my stomach called out in reply, it broke the moment's hold on me. I got up and set out in the direction of a tuna sandwich for lunch. It was always tuna for lunch at the beach. Once, when much older, eating a tuna sandwich at home, I noticed that something was missing. Then it dawned on me that tuna sandwiches did not inherently have sand in them.

The Backyard

I dragged my baby blanket from the breakfast table in the dining room to the window in the TV room so I could watch them leave. The sun had woken a couple of hours earlier and was dappling the front yard through elms and maples. My sister walked in cable-knit knee-highs down the driveway to school, accompanied by other kids, and my dad backed out of the garage in a sparkly-blue car. When both my sister and the sparkly blue disappeared beyond view, it was just my mother, my blanket, and me. My blanket, Gully, was protective, reassuring, and soft. He smelled like coziness, and I rubbed him on my nose while sucking my thumb.

I pondered a truck as it drove by, leaving a plume of cloudy exhaust. Then I made a gradual return to the dining nook by the kitchen, where my mother cleaned breakfast dishes. With thumb in mouth, I plopped down next to a set of wooden blocks. I liked the blue blocks best and lined them up in front of me with my left hand. My left hand. It was a comfort to rock and hum in a monotone while taking in the vibrancy of blue blocks.

"Diana?" I startled as my mother said my name.

I looked at her face and almost didn't recognize it, pale, drained, puffy, and shadowed. I didn't respond. I needed transition time to understand the change in my mother's face. She couldn't wait that long.

"Jesus," she said.

She picked up Gully and me, returned us to the TV room, and sat us in front of *Sesame Street*. She left in search of the ironing board and wrinkled clothes. If I could have communicated how the TV made Gully and me feel, she might have brought us into the beautiful spring morning and sat us in front of the sun instead.

Sometime later, after ironing, my mother lay on the couch with *One Life to Live*. The sunny day outside balked at the dim lighting of the TV room, and the drama emanating from the loud box highlighted my mother's listlessness. Something coursed through my body like stinging lemon juice on a scratched heart.

I wanted her to play with me, but the wall of haze between us made it seem impossible. It didn't make sense to me how to connect. I couldn't find an opening to ask for something through the heavy, depressive energy that reached out in tendrils, holding me captive in a matrix of complex adult emotion. The weight of it suffocated. There was a responsibility to make it go away, but what the 'it' was and how to make it go away, I just couldn't comprehend.

I stood and toddled to the doorway because it whispered of escape. My mother didn't take notice. I crept down the hall, spying dirty ashtrays and crystal tumblers of half-drank golden liquid in the living room, and I returned to the blue blocks. I considered the blocks for a moment, but they had long since lost their draw, so I stared at dust particles suspended in the soft and sunny light filtering through the open backdoor. It filled my attention.

A warm, fresh breeze moved my curls ever so imperceptibly, and I followed its smell until I was sitting under the old apple tree next to the ramshackle garden shed in the backyard. Earthen drafts of grass and soil rose up from the ground, shattering the heavy indoor emotions and dispersing them into complete dissolution. Energy within me spiraled up, meeting the blue of the sky.

In carefree timelessness, I observed the frolic of black-capped chickadees rummaging for breakfast, I ran my finger over holes left in the bark of the apple tree by burrowing insects, I tasted the ripeness of blackberries on the breeze, and a voice, as it called, *chicka-dee-dee-dee-dee,* welcomed me into my true home.

I spent many afternoons in the backyard, playing on my own beneath the old apple tree, learning more about the world than K-8 could ever teach me. I understood the lessons and skills inherent in *Sesame Street* and *The Electric Company*, but outside, in the backyard, I gathered around me different lessons and skills which led directly to an expansive awareness of the world, the natural world; connectivity gained through sensory experience within a slow-moving, innately logical order. I understood the dance of a squirrel, I smelled rains coming long before storm clouds appeared, and I knew that a worm would not trek across the grass on a dry morning. I was not afraid of high winds or blizzards or lightning. Mine was a lesson in the inseparability of all life, a play of true connectivity, which I recognized because it turned the sting of lemons to joy.

As an undiagnosed Autistic youth, **Diana Nadeau** experienced the difficulties of living outside the box. Decades later and with great reconciliation, the gifts of neurodiverse thinking give Diana the ability to communicate unique experiential insight through writing. As an award-winning author of two children's picture books, an equity-informed mediator, and a private consultant providing support in areas of conflict resolution and cultural competence in special education, Diana brings wisdom and lived experience to cutting-edge social issues. You can find her at DianaNadeau.com.

ADULT
FICTION

Category Winner:
Mother
by Antonia Deignan

Mother

You didn't feel like you were the same weight of ash as Dad. I mean, you were smaller than him. When I'd received Dad, a year following his last inhale, he'd already been passed around a bit. He'd been pinched off by various hands here and there, cast into the salty waters of the Atlantic, cast into the dense and overgrown garden of seagrass and hydrangeas he'd planted, cast beyond the sill of here and now. But he still weighed more than you.

You died on the Sunday before Thanksgiving, and by that Thursday, you were in my closet. I placed you on a shelf near some of my jewelry, underneath my hanging sun dresses and lace tops. The funeral parlor was compassionate. Because of the shortened holiday week, the caretakers told me it would be unlikely I'd have you home by the holiday. They had a lot of incinerations already queued; they told me. But I begged them. And I pleaded with them. And I dissolved in the waiting room off the quiet formal lobby of the funeral parlor, sitting in an elegant and uncomfortable chair, not knowing what to do about anything except beg and plead.

Late on that Wednesday, I got the call, "we were able to accommodate you," she said compassionately, "you can come and pick up your mother." And I dissolved again, like the sand on Jungle beach where her coast meets your eternal surf. I dissolved like Spiderman's nemesis Sandman in the silo, the Marvel comic book character, one moment standing, the next moment crumbling into gravelly nothing, disintegrating finally.

"No, I don't need you to come with me," I then told my husband, my kids. "No, thank you." You see, I wanted you all for myself, like a blanket, like the scarf I had held every day of my first seven years, or was it nine years? The scarf I worried and wound and caressed until the day you forbade it, stole it, and burned it. I stuffed you then, mama, into the hole that scarf left in me; I stuffed you in there.

The black box (of you) was heavy (but not as heavy as Dad.) Your watch sat on top of the box in a Ziploc. The watch your granddaughter attempted to loosen from your cold, blue wrist, but couldn't because it wouldn't come off, that Sunday, and she became anxious and shook and dissolved because she's just like me, my daughter, your granddaughter, prone to liquefying. It was only a little past seven that morning, and I guess you died in that shitty hospital bed that we'd moved into your room, with your watch on, and an unresolved antibiotic on the tip of your pasty dry tongue. I thought it was a tooth. Your white oak four poster bed frame was down the hall, stacked and leaning up against a wall in someone else's abandoned apartment.

The following year I'd poured you at the ocean's shoreline, at Jungle and Dogfish bar (near your sweetie granddaughter Gabrielle). I'd dusted the beach rose bushes behind your clapboard home in Menemsha with you; your heavy powdered sugar scent held time there, held the morning fog in its place before you billowed into my nose and sickly tickled me inside, stubbornly.

Your watch made me sad. You had worn it on your left wrist, the wrist we had stood near, aside your deathbed, the wrist that refused to let go of the time. Most of your watches were modern (think Swatch brand watches) or utilitarian (think near bottom of the line, Timex), but you also had some fabulous, chic ones. I remembered a wide cuff made of tortoise shell. It had a small gold-edged clock face attached to the middle of it, and you would have worn it to go out somewhere, the symphony or the theater, or a dinner party. Another one you favored was white gold, antique. Its thin cord snaked your wrist, and a delicate ivory analog time-face with Roman numerals sat delicately attached to its middle; the face would have fit inside a Lincoln penny; it was tiny. You wore that one often. It fell modestly onto the back of your hand and swung back and forth as you typed at your desk in the basement, in your home office. It was playful, you seemed silly. You also had a heavy gold ornate bracelet that pulled apart at the top and revealed a hidden face of a timepiece only then when it was opened.

You slept with your watches on, always, and with your bracelets on too, like a gypsy, bangled in adornments, Tibetan bands, coppered chains, voodoo-ing your joint pain. Your knuckles advertised arthritis, witchy knobs of bone and flesh, a haggler's golden hands, silver, copper, brass, and turquoise, and onyx and diamonds, swollen, magnificent. Your jewelry was easily removed.

Now, I sensed you all the time, a ridiculous amount. Never could I have predicted how tethered I would become to you since that Sunday. I smelled you. Often. I tried to dispute it. For instance, I was somewhere, boarding an airplane, and suddenly, you, Chanel numeral cinq. And then I checked my surroundings, sniffed strangers next to me, whiffed chairs, the suitcases above me, and there wasn't a smidge of you. Returning to the exact spot you first caught me, I inhaled deeply, nothing. You came and went at stop signs, in my backyard, my car, my hands, my dreams.

Every single night, my dreams.

One night: I moved in. I wasn't caretaking you, not really; I was your roommate. I could sense your needs, your lists (pills, cough drops, tissues, sanitary pads, toilet paper, paper plates, index cards, stamps, shredded cheese, berries, Starbucks iced coffee, laundering, remote controlling, touching you…) I anticipated your life hacks so you wouldn't caw or cackle, or whistle or whisper, or love or hate.

I called you a crow after I'd noticed the black delicate feathers shining blue and green and yellow on your back, on your neck, in the shadows, darkly pearled in rows, your ears too smooth, your feathered coat pressed in sacred math, perfect geometry of bitterness and pain and regret; a half-eaten worm stood between your tight lips, its tail curled and flipped inward toward its navel's seam and then opposite mimicking a fishing hook's weep, you ate her without chewing, you ate her because you only thought of surviving, and then you shat, everywhere.

Your flapping wings sliced the air behind you, and hurricanes followed, washovers, breaches, violations. You hadn't noticed the chaotic winds leaving you, or you ignored them because passing wind was beneath you.

I had called you crow because of the pecking.

I had called you crow after I saw us flying, climbing higher toward midnight stars, me on your back, not falling, not failing, not dissolving, but flapping together in perfect time,

in love,

doomed.

We were all birds, with words. It's just that, I had wanted you to be my mother.

Antonia Deignan is a mother of five children by choice, a dancer by calling, and a writer by necessity. She danced professionally in Chicago and New York, until prioritizing raising her children. She eventually owned her own dance studio and directed her pre-professional dance company before a bike accident in 2018, wish-boned her path and her identity. She has multiple publications in magazine and online formats. With all five children out of the house, she mothers three Great Danes. Her memoir, *Underwater Daughter*, published by She Writes Press, releases in May 2023. Learn more at AntoniaDeignan.com

Ask No Omen
by Mark Tricarico

Ask No Omen

Chapter One

The leaden sky hadn't looked particularly threatening but, like so much else, couldn't be trusted. Paolo Fabbri, filled with dismay, still couldn't help but admire the suddenness of the storm, its quiet malignance. They had been waiting nearly an hour in the u-shaped valley, the handiwork of a glacier some 300,000 years before, and Paolo was cold. Now he would be colder. He hoped the snow wouldn't hinder the fires they would light when the plane arrived. If it arrived.

They had been debating that very point when they finally heard the drone of the approaching aircraft, the engines sounding tired, an animal in a field at the end of a long day. They moved quickly to ignite the fires; their efforts muffled by a deepening blanket of snow. Paolo was suddenly thankful they had added petrol to the wood and hay to ensure that it burned. Giancarlo, local baker and hero to all at the Christmas market, worked furiously with numb fingers at the Aldis lamp.

"Paolo." Ronald Trent, their liaison with the British SOE—the Strategic Operations Executive—pointed skyward. The black silhouette of the plane against the even blacker sky was difficult to make out, but Paolo soon found it. He hoped the fires would be visible through the weather. Snowing hard now, Paolo had to pick up his legs to walk. If the drop was scattered, as it could be even under the best of conditions, it could take hours to find it all. He saw the first parachute seconds before its cargo nearly crushed him, the swirling snow obscuring all but what was immediately in front of them.

"Fucking weather," mumbled Trent. Paolo had been impressed by the man's Italian. He looked to be an athlete of some sort—cropped hair, powerful arms, square jaw, and all the rest of it—with a facility for languages. He was also an accomplished swearer. Paolo understood. It was an important haul.

They had been desperate for weapons, and the frequency of airdrops had been sporadic at best. The SOE had dropped Trent in weeks before to coordinate communications among partisan groups and the Allies, schedule airdrops, and train them in weapons and sabotage. Finally, there was something like a system in place, and supplies would, they had been assured, begin to come more regularly. It had taken time for military leadership to recognize the strategic value of the partisans, but finally, it seemed that they had.

"We'll be lucky if we find it all by next Tuesday," Trent grunted. It was getting difficult to talk and walk at the same time, the snow requiring greater effort to negotiate.

"I think I saw some end up behind that ridge." Paolo followed the SOE man's extended arm. The ridge looked closer than it really was Paolo knew. He groaned.

He started off toward the escarpment, another dark silhouette in a grand vista of dark silhouettes. They were looking for 51 Sten guns, two cases of grenades, ammunition, incendiary bombs, explosives, and food and clothing—nineteen parachutes in all. Once they were sure it all had come down, they extinguished the flames, and the eight-man team began fanning out across the valley. They had a charcoal hauler's wagon pulled by two horses. Getting everything out would be nearly as difficult as finding it.

Paolo took a flashlight from his coat pocket and flicked it on; impenetrable night suddenly turning to bafflingly bright day, his confusion clearing as the firing began. Muzzle flashes like bursting flowers betrayed the German position behind a stand of oak, now no longer needing to remain hidden. Then chaos, followed by the unmistakable sound of slaughter.

Paolo fell to the ground, sinking into the soft snow. There was a muffled shout—German—an unrelenting stream of gunfire, cries that abruptly ended. His mind raced. With every crack and pop he expected the searing pain of the bullet he knew must come.

Move! He knew he had to but couldn't. It wasn't fear. He didn't quite know what it was, only that his limbs wouldn't respond. He took a breath and thought he recalled a mountain stream somewhere nearby. A mountain stream. Ah, that sounded nice. But such idyllic places ceased to exist in 1939. He had to try to find it. It would be freezing, but the alternative...

He had been on his way to the ridge when the attack began, so he hoped he was now outside the German concentration of fire. He stayed as low as he could, praying the snow was deep enough to conceal him. Moving as quickly as he dared, he tried to picture the scene before him, recalling the terrain from the drop reconnaissance two weeks earlier. If he remembered correctly, there was a large area of bearberry scrub some fifty meters ahead that might offer some cover. He wouldn't be able to stay there for long, but he could at least hide for a moment to gather his thoughts. He pushed on, his breathing erratic now with the effort, thunderous in his ears.

The gunfire trailed off behind him, then stopped. He could sense their movement. They were searching, the element of surprise now spent. He caught hints of light sweeping the valley. Another shout, a single gunshot. In his mind's eye, he flew above the scene, pictured where he was and where they were, the scrub just ahead now.

"Dort!"

The light illuminated the bearberry, close enough to touch. He had been right, had always had a good memory. He finally felt the bullet he knew must come. And then he felt nothing.

Chapter Two

"They   lost   Trent."
"Ah shit. When?"

"The drop on the fourteenth."

"Just Trent?"

Alan Thompson, Deputy Director, Special Operations branch of the OSS—Office of Strategic Services—shook his large head. The permanent cigarette in his mouth, perpetually half-smoked, waved like a maestro's baton. He was a big man in both directions. "Near as we can tell, they got them all. And everything that came down."

"Jesus. How?"

"If I had to guess, someone told them. I could be wrong. It could've been any number of things. Sloppy security, somebody with cock in hand looking to get laid. But I don't think so. Besides, we're still babes in the woods as far as SOE is concerned, so they don't tell us much. Especially when they fuck up."

If true, this was very bad news. Dante Kral looked out the window. Rain. Again. People, buildings, everything blurred and distorted; what was what, and who was who? He couldn't tell and thought with bitter amusement there might be some metaphor in that. The drops filed across the glass, soldiers marching downhill. He slid a finger down the window, making it squeak.

He and Trent first met at OSS headquarters in Algiers, becoming friends later after crossing paths in the various agent-training programs the SOE and OSS shared. He was lean and hard, in his early forties. He looked younger but felt older. His brown hair was cut short. Striking blue eyes over a nose he thought a little too bulbous at the end. It was Kral, as in *King*, half Czech, half Italian on his mother's side. Not so enjoyable to be Czech these days. His mother had been a reader, favoring the deep contemplative classics, her nature straying to the bleak. Dante held her responsible for his own outlook, which landed considerably south of sunny. Raised in America, he had felt out of place.

"I need you to go in, Dante." Dante nodded, and said nothing. "I know you've only just returned from Istanbul." Two weeks earlier, in fact, and he was due for a rest. He had gone to Turkey to *infiltrate and extenuate subversive action in the old Ottoman and Austro-Hungarian empires*, end quote. And he had done it well.

"We have to assume the entire network is compromised, so we'll need to drop you in with another W/T guy. After a little refresher at Camp X."

So, reestablish wireless communications as well. Dante remained silent. He had always been a thinker, weighing his options before he spoke. It never failed to make Thompson anxious. The man hated silence.

"You can say no."

"Not really."

"No, not really. You know I wouldn't ask if we didn't need this. Hell," Thompson continued, making his case. "Let's call a spade a spade. It's a fucking mess. We have Socialist brigades; we have Communist brigades. We have Christian Democrats. And they all hate the king and Badoglio, which of course, we officially don't. It's too political, at least according to Washington and London. Churchill thinks they need to stop fucking around with the politics and start aligning with military objectives. And FDR agrees. So, we agree."

Dante looked at his friend. He could see the stress in Thompson's eyes, knew he was feeling guilty, and forgave him instantly. He smiled and Thompson, clearly relieved, did the same. Two smiles meaning two very different things.

Carrying the name of a small hill town in southern Italy, **Mark Tricarico** spent many years as a copywriter in advertising agencies from Madison Avenue to San Francisco before jumping to the worlds of technology and finance. A former United States Naval officer, he holds degrees in finance and law, and became fascinated with the Italian resistance during World War II when restoring a centuries-old house in Italy. He can be found at LinkedIn.

Burying Legacy
by Rebecca Marks Rudy

Burying Legacy

Chapter One

They head into the unknown, all of them uprooted one of them unmoored.

Minutes and miles tick by. On a good day, the drive due west from Chicago to Timmons Prairie takes a breezy couple of hours—where the longer the journey, the greater the gap between houses. Where red barns and domed silos gleam against a sprawling sea of green and gold. Where field after field passes in alternate patterns: beans and corn, corn and beans. Where the pavement points impossibly straight while the farmland stretches unfathomably flat.

But there are no more good days, and they are prepared for this.

Somewhat.

Carina sedated her father at the start—before the car ride, even before the flight out of JFK. She needed him mellow, tempered a bit but not dead weight. Now, hours later—she labors to count how many—the meds have mostly worn off. The rocking returns. She feels it beginning again, his agitation soaring. The tension and twitching. And next, the raking—his fingernails along his knees. She peeks at his reflection: his mouth pumps, his lips forming shapes without any sound. Not a single trace.

Until: "Need to whizz, need to whizz, need to whizz."

In a panic, Carina veers. The tires screech to a stop.

She jumps up, races around to the passenger side, pulls Pops to a stand, and hurries his hand to unzip. How is she to hold it, this hidden part of him? Flaccid, shriveled, so strangely pale. She guides his grip beyond tabs and elastic and waits. Her eyes rove, looking to land anywhere else; she listens for the trickle. He sways, she braces. She listens and waits some more. She strains through the glare of the glass, focusing in on the back. On Ellie, holding firm, neck curved, eyes fixed. Also waiting. She shouldn't have to see this. No one should. But Jesus, a little help here would be good. Carina kicks one heel against the other. Twice, and again. Still no trickle. Like every other attempt, a false alarm. She buckles Pops in, and they press on.

Soon: "I'm whizzing, I'm whizzing, I'm whizzing."

Carina claws the wheel. In the rearview mirror, she registers her daughter's alarm. "It's okay," she says. "He's wearing a diaper. As backup." No being discreet anymore. No dancing around this, some ardently guarded secret. "He'll be changed whenever we get there."

"Don't you mean if we ever get there?"

"Ellie, not the time—" Carina says. "And remember, this move is not only for him." Her foot clamps down on the gas. "It's also about you."

She tunes out Ellie's groan from behind.

But she can't tune out the tapping coming from Pops' side. She spins to the sound—his hand against the window. It could be his head next. Or maybe the elbow flapping or the scab picking. Or maybe something entirely new. Who knows? Music might calm him. She asks Ellie to load the playlist. First up, Johnny Cash.

"Pops, can you hear it?"

"Hear it. Hear it. Hear it here." His rocking now matches the rhythm. "Here. Here. Here."

One song rolls right into the next. It's working. Carina glances at the clock. They should be there within the hour. The sun slides out from behind a cloud, and she digs in her bag for glasses, drowning beneath lipsticks and tissues and a picture-filled pamphlet with Lorna's instructions. Focused on the road and the wheel and the mess on her lap, she doesn't see him lean and then lunge. She doesn't catch him fumbling with the latch. Not before he starts banging, badgering at the door.

"Pops! What the hell?" Carina shrieks. "Are you trying to get yourself killed?"

She swerves onto the shoulder. The car halts. Dust rises and floats.

"Ellie, grab Pops' meds and some water. Or we'll never make it."

"See, what did I tell—"

"Please—"

She hears Ellie rummage through Pops' bag for his pills and twists around to retrieve them. But she pauses, running the numbers. Two would be overkill. A half dose is enough. She chooses one, and sends one back. "Put this in your mouth, Pops," she says, securing the capsule and water, each in a separate hand. "Take a sip. Swallow."

But Pops doesn't. He shoves the pill between his lips. Then spits it clear onto the dash. Carina asks Ellie for the spare and tries again. This time Pops chokes. As he sputters, Ellie, somehow unruffled, produces another. It goes down and stays down.

Carina gives this a minute to be sure. In waiting, she brushes away her tears, their wetness staining her skin. She tries to name them, these droplets, before they disappear. Anger? Grief? Or guilt? She doesn't know anymore; she'd rather be numb.

She starts the engine and urges her father to settle. She squeezes his hand, letting her sweating touch linger. He answers by pitching and fidgeting until the medication slowly takes hold. Here and there, she steals a glimpse of him, his blue eyes—same silver-streaked shade as Ellie's—his grown glazed and vacant. But this isn't him, Doctor Thomas Holden, her beloved Pops, beside her. In his place, a child. An errant boy, entombed in an alien body.

At last, the endless drive finds an end: Sunnydale.

Carina parks. She pulls her shoulder blades back into a satisfying crackle. Then flexes her toes. Again, flex and release, craving sweet, fleeting reprieve. She presses her forehead and temples with her fingertips. Finally, looking out, she draws in a breath. This is it. This is where Pops lives now. A two-storied building in a mix of stone and shingle, up front a circular drive, and on one side, off to the right, a gated courtyard garden, this the winning feature. Standing alone on the entryway pavers, a woman waves, and smiles. Must be Lorna; she did say she'd be here for their arrival, however late in the day. Carina returns the wave before swinging open her door and stepping into the summer swelter.

Lorna bounds toward them, everything about her bouncing—her breasts and hips, her cheeks and chin, and most of all, her words. "Oh, welcome, welcome!" she chirps.

Such enviable vigor. Carina searches her daughter for a knowing smile or tiny smirk. But Ellie goes on rolling out her neck and stretching her hips and wanting little from her other than space. Lorna, coming in hot and stopping only for hugs, strides right up to uncoil Pops from the passenger seat.

"How was the trip?" she asks him.

No reply.

Unbothered, Lorna entwines her arm with his. An arm long and lean, once thicker with a swimmer's strength. The loss happening so fast. Too fast, really, to keep track. At what point, in all of it, had he become so bowed, so bent?

"We are very, very happy to have you with us!" Lorna chirps again.

Nothing.

"I'm care manager here at Sunnydale. Anything you need, come see me."

Nothing.

"We have a cozy corner room all set up for you, Doc."

Nothing.

Lorna's whole face brightens. "With a window!"

Carina teases a grin. A prime room, a pleasant enough place. And more than pleasant, safe. But her smile shrinks when she watches her Pops, this giant man-child, grasping for the unfamiliar. As Lorna leads them inside, Carina looks down at her hand, flipping it side to side. A thin hand, but tough. Like his. Nails she keeps short, also like his. A hand that used to fit right into his, but not the one he takes.

She dips her thumbs into her pockets and surveys the space, a page pulled straight from the pamphlet: the foyer with faux-wood floors; the pair of soft-lit lamps; to the left, a sitting room with two patterned sofas; the upright piano and painted-brick fireplace; the full-bloom flowers offsetting the antiseptic scent. Also, as in the photos, residents enjoying their afternoon tea. Some sit. Others snooze. One delighted lady waltzes. No partner, no problem.

Lorna makes introductions along the way. Carina, trailing with Ellie, tenses each time someone passes. But Pops doesn't blurt a word, thank god. How long has it been? A month or two. Maybe more. She misses the sound of his voice—his old voice. Not the one barking unfiltered filth to anyone at any time. "There's a fat old cunt," or, "you're one goddamned ugly turd-eating shit-bird." She used to chase these with apologies, explaining away his illness, but never erasing the shame. Silence is better. No matter how sharp the sting.

At the end of the corridor, they come to Pops' room. Pops heads to the window with Lorna. She peels the coral-leaf curtain to its edge; he suctions a palm to the glass. Reaching for what? All that exists, as far as any eye can see is this: grass and trees and field upon field. Waiting in the doorway, Carina looks on, afraid to cry and even more afraid not to.

Rebecca Marks Rudy comes to fiction by way of non-fiction. She has been featured on Discovery Health Channel and in *People Magazine*, and her work has appeared in *Triathlete, Outside, MetroSports,* and *Motherwell* magazines. Her next project follows a swimmer lost at sea—much like the one she can view from her writer's perch. She considers gazing out the window crucial to the creative process. Please feel free to visit Rebecca-Marks-Rudy.com for more.

CENTRAL AVENUE
BY CATHERINE BATOR

Central Avenue

It was 2008 and I was lucky – at the onset of the Great Recession – to have a job at all, even though it meant waking up at two in the morning to get to work by four.

I was a sales assistant at the Los Angeles Wholesale Produce Mart. It wasn't the kind of job I dreamt about as I worked my way through school, but I reminded myself every day that a girl who had spent her college days reading early medieval French manuscripts and English Victorian poetry couldn't be picky. Somehow, I thought those fields of study would put me on the fast track to some unspecified glamour job. It turns out that no one gives a damn about your exquisitely liberal education.

Working at the Mart meant I had to drag myself out of bed and into a shower at an hour when other people my age were getting home from a night of dancing. It was a painful adjustment. The middle of the night is a cruel time to wield a hair dryer and apply eyeliner, but I eventually got into a routine, and my coffee requirement dwindled down to two cups from a tremor-inducing six.

Then about two months into this hell of my own making, a completely unexpected thing happened. I began to enjoy it. I loved cruising the empty freeway from my Echo Park studio apartment past the ghostly Bunker Hill high-rises, defined in the fog by the lights in their idle offices, and I delighted in being awake while the city slept around me.

Every morning I made my way from the misty Alameda offramp through the silent Central Avenue dead zone to the Produce District. As I got close to the Mart, my Honda Put-Put would be surrounded by low-growling semis, and I became a minnow darting through a pod of whales, trying to outrun the gunk spewing from their blowholes. At 9ᵗʰ Street, the pod turned left, and I went straight to the employee entrance, where Ernesto Gomez would wave me through, never smiling, always the consummate security professional.

From the gate, I drove between the Mart's loading docks, where cherries and onions sat in crates, waiting to go to restaurants and stores. It was an international airport for edible plant life. Plums and artichokes arrived from all over the world, then went to their terminals and waited for connecting flights. My employer, Shaw Brothers Fine Fruits and Vegetables, was just one of many businesses, each one a different carrier with its own boarding gates. If you were a high-priced heirloom tomato from Italy, you flew business class on your way to Spago. If you were a lowly banana from Mexico, you flew coach and had a layover of four or five days while you turned yellow from frustration.

I parked around the corner from the docks, grabbed a cup of coffee in the break room and took it to my little glass booth in the middle of the sales floor where I collected paperwork from the staff. They were all men, known by the produce they sold: the Tomato Guy, the Orange and Pineapple guy, and the Apple Man. Apple Man was the reigning king because apples were the bread and butter of Shaw Brothers.

Tito Cantú, the Apple Man, may have been King of the Salesmen, but I was Queen of the Sales Floor. Without me, I'm not sure what would have made these guys smile. They sang songs of unrequited love to me, brought me strange little gifts like Hello Kitty socks and a hands-free umbrella hat, and of course, served me little plates of the ripest, most succulent fruit in Los Angeles. It was not lost on me that I was the token blonde goddess at Shaw brothers.

I think it was due to my exotic appearance that they felt responsible for my safety, warning me about gang warfare in the "barrio" and escorting me across the street where I occasionally grabbed a burger at McDonald's. My parents – living in Minnesota at the time – had no idea their daughter was working in the barrio. My dad was transferred to Minneapolis during my junior year at UCLA, and my parents left their now "mature" daughter behind, assuming she would have the good sense to keep to the Westside – her natural habitat.

But here I was at Shaw Brothers with a bunch of jokers who flirted with me without ever calling me by my first name. I was always Miss Fairbrother, even though I made a point my first week of asking each one of them to call me Kelly. By the second week, I had given up, and I also came to realize they could only make little jokes (mostly of a sexual nature), whistle at me, and bring me presents if they kept a certain distance. They were the schoolboys, and I was the sexy young teacher. I couldn't decide if I was flattered or embarrassed.

I had been earning my keep this way for about six months and finding ever more advantages to working the early shift – like fitting in daytime Italian classes at Pasadena City College after work – when I had my first brush with the violent world that swirled around me.

It was a foggy June morning, and I was enjoying my pre-dawn swim with the pod down Central Avenue. As I came to 9th Street, the pod went with the current, and I headed for shore. At the first hint of flashing red lights reflected on my windshield, I slowed. As I rolled ahead, I could see LAPD black-and-whites parked all over the street in a crazy zigzag. There must have been ten of them in front of McDonald's, across from the Produce Mart's employee entrance.

I neared the police blockade and saw the yellow tape blocking my way. I slowed. An officer approached the passenger side of the Put-Put, and I rolled down the window.

"What's the trouble, officer?" I said. He was a good-looking straight arrow of a guy, weighed down by a police tool belt that included at least one gun and a lot of other intimidating paraphernalia.

"Gang activity," he said. "You'll need to go back to 7th and then over to Alameda."

The word "gang" shot through me like the Taser on his belt, and my muscles went weak. Up until this moment, I had assumed my schoolboys were being ridiculously overprotective of me. "Gangs?" was all I could say.

He saw the stunned look on my face – a look he had probably seen before. Middle-class horror of lower-class violence. "We have cars patrolling the area, Miss. It's safe to go about your business. No access to this section of Central for about three or four hours, though. You work in the Produce Mart?"

"Yes, officer, I usually use this entrance," I said, but by now, I had spotted two bodies on the ground in back of him, and I couldn't take my eyes off them.

"You can enter off Palmetto," he said.

The crime scene was lit by five or six portable lights placed around the corpses. One was shining directly in front of me on the closest victim – a skinny boy with a shaved head and a blood-soaked white T-shirt pushed up to his chest. His stomach was covered with a tattoo of large black gothic letters.

𝔅 𝔑 𝔒

But it was his face that made me stare – it was the face of a sleeping child. Asleep forever on the blacktop on Central Avenue, blood not yet dried on his white shirt, in the spotlight of a barrio crime scene. The other, lying a few feet away, was round as a cherub, his face turned away from me, his head lying in a halo of blood.

Catherine Bator has worked for comedy writers at Paramount and MGM studios and later in corporate communications—experiences that can only be described as the polar extremes of the work world. Her novel, *A Good, Hard Slap*, was shortlisted for the 2021 First Pages Prize, and the first chapter was published in Embark, a literary journal for novelists. She was a semi-finalist for the 2021 Eludia Award for a previous novel. She lives high above San Francisco Bay with her husband and fearsome fox terrier, Buster Keaton. She can be reached at catherinebator@me.com.

GIRL WITH A PAST
BY SHERRI LEIGH JAMES

Girl with a Past

PROLOGUE

Berkeley, May 1969

The day I was murdered, I thought all I had to fear was being tear-gassed on campus.

With our faces covered in paisley bandannas, we looked like gangs of marauding outlaws swarming the campus instead of university students. We braved swooping helicopters and air filled with tear gas to get to class on the south side near Sather Gate.

I avoided that side of campus as much as possible, but I had one class in Dwinelle Hall, near Sather Gate. Just outside the Gate, rows of bayonet-bearing National Guardsmen, with their faces hidden by gas masks, kept troublemakers off campus. The problem was they couldn't tell just who the troublemakers were. All us hippies looked alike to them.

I crossed Strawberry Creek and was almost back to the relative peace of Northside when I heard the sound of slapping helicopter blades headed straight for my position. I pulled a damp bandanna over my nose and mouth, put my head down, and made a run for it.

Driven by the increasing noise of helicopters, I scrambled toward a grove of redwood trees. I had made maybe twenty feet when my throat and eyes began to burn, tears cutting my visibility. Almost there, almost to the North Gate, my foot hit a pile of leaves, and I slid, landing on my ass.

A strong hand grabbed my arm and pulled me to my feet.

"You okay?" he muttered behind his handkerchief.

He towed me through the trees into the nearest building. We stumbled down the wide hall to a drinking fountain and splashed our faces with cool water. My back to the wall, I slid to the floor and tried to breathe.

My rescuer plopped down beside me. We both gasped for air, wiped our eyes, and blew our noses. When I could see again, I noticed that even bloodshot eyes and a running nose failed to lessen the attractiveness of my new friend. Dark chocolate brown hair curled around his ears and neck; blue eyes matched his faded jeans.

My breathing came easier, easy enough for me to speak. "I'm Lexi." I rasped and extended my hand.

"Derek." He took my hand and held it. "Are you hurt?"

I pulled my hand away and shook my head.

"You fell pretty hard. You didn't break anything?"

"I'll have an awesome bruise on my ass." I drew blonde hair away from my face, and tucked long locks behind my ears and into the neck of my fur-lined jacket. "I'm okay. Just sick of this routine."

"Yeah. I can dig it," Derek said. "You would think we were causing the trouble."

Certainly, Governor Reagan thought we were dangerous criminals—or the enemy. Claiming that the Berkeley campus was "a haven for communist sympathizers, protesters, and sexual deviants," Reagan had sent in the National Guard to deal with us.

How far things had disintegrated since December of 1964.

The party, later known as a "sit-in," in Sproul Plaza had started four and a half years earlier when Mario Savio removed his shoes to climb onto the roof of the police car holding Jack Weinberg. Savio then invited students and faculty to sit down around the vehicle.

Military recruiters, industrial headhunters, and campus organizations set up tables lining one edge of Sproul Plaza just outside Sather Gate. Weinberg had been manning a table for CORE, Congress for Racial Equality when university police placed him in the car. Thirty-two hours of peaceful sitting by three thousand people while Savio delivered rousing speeches ended with Weinberg being released and the crowd dispersing. The Free Speech Movement born that day on the Berkeley campus soon morphed into an anti-war, anti-establishment movement.

The People's Park crisis that Reagan now responded to with a heavy hand had minimal participation by students or faculty until the National Guard started shooting people. The 1967 Summer of Love in San Francisco had drawn thousands of young people to the Bay Area. Some of the ones who had wandered over to Berkeley from the Haight had camped on a vacant plot of land near the campus and owned by the university. Park inhabitants and local residents began protests when the university decided to clear the site of the campers and vegetable gardens in order to build a parking lot and athletic fields. Thanks to the governor, the National Guard not only brought bayonets, rifles, and shotguns, they also filled the skies with helicopters spewing tear gas.

Some of us just wanted to go to class and graduate.

I stood up and adjusted my book bag on my shoulder. "Thank you for the rescue."

Derek scrambled to his feet, hurried to open the door, and walked beside me out of the building through the North Gate.

No sign of helicopters, but the smell of tear gas lingered. Masked students and faculty—after years of interrupted campus life—rushed by us, attempting to go about their usual business in a war zone.

"Where ya headed?" He stuck close to my side as I rushed across Hearst Avenue before the light turned red.

Aw, for chrissakes. Yeah, he rescued me, but did that mean I had to be nice to him? Why couldn't I be a bitch without guilt-tripping myself? He was exactly the excessively handsome kind of guy I wanted to avoid.

"Thanks again. I do appreciate you helping me." I forced a smile and waved. "Ciao."

I lengthened my stride; maybe he'd give up. I glanced to my left; he was hanging in there. His legs were even longer than mine. I wouldn't lose him easily.

He caught my eye and smiled that charming, crooked grin. Oh man, those crystal blue eyes. And dimples.

I couldn't help myself. I returned the smile.

He grinned. "Groovy." He waved at the tables and chairs on the wide patio of the Euclid Café. "Coffee?"

I nodded and followed him to a table.

"Sit, please. Cream?"

I nodded.

"Sugar?"

I nodded again, dropped my book bag next to one of the chairs, and sat down.

He walked to the line of students and faculty waiting to order.

A newspaper left on the table headlined another Zodiac killing. A photo of his latest victim headed the front-page story, and a copy of a letter purportedly from the Zodiac was next to the photo.

I couldn't handle any more evidence of our fucked-up world that day. I moved the newspaper to a nearby table.

Derek returned with two steaming mugs of coffee before I had a chance to reconsider befriending a stranger. Especially a handsome one. He placed both cups on the table and passed me a handful of sugar packets.

"So . . . where do you live?" he asked.

At least he didn't ask me, "what's your sign?" Or "what's your major?" But then the smears of acrylic paint on my bell-bottom jeans might have given my art major away.

"Up the hill." I waved up toward the top of the Berkeley hills.

"Headed home?"

"Yeah. I've got a lot of work to do." I rubbed dried paint off my finger.

"What're you painting?"

"Kinda abstract nudes in landscapes."

He raised an eyebrow. "Like cubist nudes descending staircases?"

"I'm not Picasso or Braque. Landscapes, not interiors."

He flashed that damn smile revealing dimples again. "I'd love to see them."

That I ignored. "What's your thing?"

"Architecture."

"And you escaped the Environmental Design building?" I asked with a smile. "Don't they keep would-be architects chained to their drafting tables? I see people working in there twenty-four hours a day."

"True, too true." He sipped his coffee and then grinned. "Couldn't hack it, had to get out and find a pretty girl to rescue."

I drank the last of my coffee. "Thank you." I forced a smile.

I wasn't going to violate my new agreements with myself. No more handsome and charming men. Too dangerous for my bruised heart. Women throw themselves at men like this one.

"I really do have to get to work."

He drained his cup and stood up. "May I walk with you?"

I shrugged an "if you want to," and picked up my bag.

Sherri Leigh James graduated from UC Berkeley in 1969. The late 60's in the San Francisco Bay Area were wild and adventurous times filled with sex, drugs, and rock 'n' roll. Her adventures, and those of her friends, while attending Cal provide material for *Girl With A Past*. She became a prominent Los Angeles interior designer whose clients included well-known figures in the entertainment industry, billionaire families, and even mob bosses. Her intimate view of the private world of the rich and famous inspires her new mystery series, *Blood Red* and *Iced Blue*, introducing interior designer Cissy Huntington. SherriLeighJames.com.

SING YET OF ELMS
BY L. DAWN JACKSON

Sing Yet of Elms

Wet branches slashed across Kenzie's palms as she stumbled between them. The air rasped in her aching lungs, undergrowth grabbing her feet in the predawn gloom. She had given up on stealth long ago. Even if they couldn't hear or see her, they could smell her. Her heart pounded until it felt like it would break her ribs, but she couldn't stop. The deep howls still surrounded her, hunting her. Sunlight struggled to force its way through the heavy fog, shrouding everything in a surreal semi-gloom.

She broke through the trees, nearly losing her footing as underbrush and roots gave way to overgrown grass. Relief made her sob. The only trace of humans was the wooden boardwalk wending from the edge of a steep drop-off out into a sea of fog. Hair whipped her face as she risked a glance behind her. The howls were louder, answering each other from behind her and from either side. It was almost as if the wolves were herding her, trapping her against this steep drop-off where her only escape was a wet boardwalk. She might step foot on there and have rotten wood crumble out from under her. But they were still coming. Her muscles and lungs burned, and they were still coming. Her head and heart pounded, and they were still coming. Blood ran down her face and matted in her hair, smeared her hands and her arms and through the tatters in her clothing, and they were still coming. No matter what she did, *they were still coming.*

Kenzie gulped down air and flung herself onto the boardwalk. The worn tread of her sneakers slipped on the wet wood, and pain jolted through her as she slipped to hands and knees. Before she was even on her feet again, she was scrambling forward. Faint smears of pink stained the wood where she had fallen. She didn't notice. Her eyes were fixed ahead into the blank fog, trying to convince herself that safety lay just inside. If she could just get far enough inside the fog, maybe…!

Her heel struck the edge of a stair. Her slick sneaker slipped out from under her, and Kenzie's tailbone hit wood hard enough to make her teeth rattle. Crashing down three stairs, she careened across the wet planks. The walkway turned sharply to the right. Kenzie flailed, trying to slow herself, but she shot over the edge of the walk. Both hands slapped around a railing support with bruising force. Dangling over the edge, the tops of trees far below her, she clung to the post as the howls ricocheted through the fog.

Those howls distorted around her as Kenzie dangled far above the trees. Her arms and shoulders ached. Desperately, she shifted her grip on the railing post, trying to relieve the pressure on her hands without losing her purchase on the slick wood. Tears pricked the corners of her eyes as she stared into the gray fog. Suspended between sky and trees, all she could do was plead with the universe for help and hold on.

Shadows flitted through the fog. The walkway rumbled as something large pounded on the planks. Kenzie's hands slipped, and she fought desperately to hang on. A cry welled up in her throat, but she swallowed it down. If it were the wolves, the sound would tell them exactly where to find her.

"Hoy! More wolves to the north!" someone called. More shouts answered, accompanied by darting shadows and pounding feet. People passed over her head, glimpses of shoes flashing between the slats. Several sharp twangs thrummed in the air, along with more shouts. The howls changed to animal screams of pain and rage.

The confusion seemed to go on and on. It felt as if her shoulders were separating from the joints, and the pain in her hands was worsening. The wood felt slicker. She couldn't wait any longer.

"Hey! Somebody!" she shouted into a lull in the confusion. There was no answer. Kenzie took a deep breath and punched the air out. "***HEY!***"

Footsteps halted. Three pairs of boots shaded the walk overhead. Kenzie panted with relief.

"Down here!" she shouted again, just as an enormous dark shape appeared on the walkway. The boots disappeared. The snarl that tore the air made her heart rise to her throat. The vicious sound died in a feeble gurgle as something dark and hot dripped between the slats in front of her face. Kenzie refused to think about it. If she did, she might be sick. The walkway rumbled as something large rolled across it. An enormous ball of black fur dropped off the edge of the boards a couple of feet from her. She made the mistake of watching it fall to the swirling gray below. Kenzie felt the blood rush from her face at the height. She didn't even have to summon the scream. It welled up from her toes and tore the air, loud enough to make the shouting start up again. A shadow dropped onto the planks, and a deep blue eye appeared in the space between slats. For just an instant, it widened, then disappeared. Large hands closed around her wrists.

"I will not let you fall," a strong, masculine voice assured her. "I cannot pull you up from here. You must let go of the post."

Strong hands held her tightly. Reflexively, she gripped his forearms in return. The powerful muscles under her hand were reassuring, but his skin was strangely slick; she couldn't get a good purchase. She tried anyway until her hands cramped and her bones creaked in protest.

A soothing sense flowed along his words and into her mind. She inhaled deeply… and sighed it out. "I am going to release your right hand, just long enough to get around the post, then I will pull you up. Do you understand?"

Cold rushed through Kenzie's blood. What choice did she have? Everything hurt, from her hands to her thighs, and her muscles were shaking. Kenzie nodded, then realized he couldn't see her.

"Yes." She choked the word past her heart in her throat. It sounded a lot steadier than she expected. That helped to steady her, too, and she focused on breathing for a moment.

"On the count. Three…two…one…!" The hand gripping hers disappeared. Her hand slipped away from his arm, despite her frantic attempts to cling to him. She dangled above the trees, supported only by the hand of a stranger.

Kenzie swung back and forth, dangling precariously by the strength of a single hand. Her head swam as she looked below her, and the tops of the trees seemed to rush up to meet her. A strangled whimper sounded in her throat.

"*Tiyane*! Look up! Look at me!" the voice ordered, a layer of fear in his tone. Kenzie flung her head back as she swung in space. There was a face. The same indigo-blue eyes peered down at her. Flung on his belly, flat on the boards, his other arm reached down for hers. On the next swing, she reached for his hand; the sound of skin slapping skin reverberated through the foggy stillness, and a smile broke on his face. Inch by inch, he moved back, never taking his gaze off hers. Inch by slow inch, the walkway came closer. The edge of the boards scraped along her arms and face, and she could not have cared less. Her jeans snagged and stitches tore, but her rescuer got his arms under hers and lifted. He dropped back onto the walkway, holding her close to his chest. The thundering heartbeat and ragged breathing beneath her ear matched Kenzie's own. She was content to lie there, eyes closed, soaking up her rescuer's warmth and listening to the soft murmur of his voice. He had a beautiful voice. It was vaguely familiar, as were the strange words, like shadows of a half-remembered dream. She let her mind drift into it, the walkway fading into a wilder world.

L. Dawn Jackson began writing stories as soon as they a pencil in her chubby baby hand. She was selected as a mentee in the inaugural 2021 Romance Authors Mentorship Program through Romance Writers of America. She is also a 2021 and 2022 finalist in the San Francisco Writers Contest. She lives at the top of the American Rocky Mountains with two miracle children, her amazing husband, a lupus diagnosis, and an ever-increasing knitting stash.

SOMETHING SPECTACULAR
BY MAREN FEWEL

Something Spectacular

Prelude:

It's been a few months, but I still get nightmares.

Sometimes I'll see the ring, the diamond catching sunlight and transforming it into tiny rainbows. It's pristine and shiny and brand new. I'll watch it glitter on my finger as I turn the key in the doorknob.

Then I'll hear shouts. Mine, his, and hers when I walked in on them. My fiancé will swear, Katrina will pull up the sheets. The image is still haunting.

Other nights, I'll hear screams. My own and my mother's when she lost control of the car. Metal will crunch, and I'll see her lifeless form. No amount of applied pressure will stop the imagined blood, and I'll feel just as helpless in the dream as I did then.

Then the ring and my hands will be stained red. No matter how much I wash, blood stays in the crevices between the swirling metal and the princess-cut gem.

It'll take me a few minutes to remind myself that it's not real. Well, it was real, but it's over now. That was a different life, and it shattered half a world away.

If there is time for me to go back to sleep, I'll turn on music—maybe Chopin's "Nocturne No. 2, Op. 9" or Bach's "Prelude No. 1" or maybe something else—until the sun rises on the City of Music, and I rise with it.

Chapter 1:

My itchy white wig slips when I scratch at it for the tenth time this afternoon. I can feel it tying my naturally dark hair underneath into knots, even though I recently cut it short, as one does when seeking life change. Before approaching the next tourist, I tug up my breeches that sag in all the wrong places.

"*Guten tag*," I say through a forced smile. After a month in this position, I'm better at the language, but my accent is still rough. The couple looks American, though, which is why I picked them. I switch to English.

"Interested in seeing a concert while you are in Vienna? Classical music capital of the world!"

The woman accepts the pamphlet and oohs and aahs over the glossy pictures of the interior of the famous opera house. With its exterior as my backdrop, I launch into my recitation of the performances and the event times and how you do not want to miss this special opportunity.

The man cuts me off.

"We have tickets to something else." He shoves the pamphlet back at me. Rotund and with sweat stains the size of salad plates under his arms, the man doesn't seem to be particularly enjoying his vacation.

Most of my advances are rejected, so I don't take responses like his personally. Even if someone accepts a flyer with a promise to think about it, more often than not, I see them crumple the paper and dump it in the first trash can they see. Not that I've checked, but I bet that bin is seventy-five percent pamphlets.

It's hard not to think of my work as futile. I get paid, though, so I keep pushing pamphlets.

Retreating to the shade of the *Wiener Staatsoper*, the Vienna State Opera House, I watch the couple hurry away. They stop a moment later, and the woman whips out a camera to take a picture of the building, as so many tourists like her do.

While I take a sip from my water bottle, my coworker and friend, Sophia, bounces over to me. She's dressed like me and the other half dozen workers.

Our "uniforms" are Mozart-esque costumes: red button-up coats, black breeches, once-white knee socks, and powdered wigs. We're modeled after a painting of Mozart, the reproduction of which is plastered on every souvenir available in this city.

We look ridiculous, but I guess that's kind of the point. We are part of the tourist trap, too.

Sophia, however, can actually almost pull it off. A petite, aspiring opera star, she has the voice of an angel and sings with more power than one would think possible for someone so small. She hails from Berlin, but since her father is English, she speaks the language perfectly. Her fluency has been a lifesaver for me.

We became friends over a shared desire to perform inside the opera house—her as a prima donna and me in the orchestra pit. Standing outside advertising the talents of others is a special kind of torture.

But my days in these shadows are numbered.

"Ready for round two, Morgen?" She picks up her own water bottle. "How are you feeling about tomorrow? I bet you can't wait to get back in there." She nods towards the building, her white wig bobbing.

"So ready."

Yesterday I auditioned for the State Opera Orchestra in the preliminary round. More prelims are being held today, and tomorrow I'm on to the semi-finals.

"I think it went really well," I tell her. "I felt good about my solo and they had me perform four excerpts. I must have been playing for almost ten minutes—and it seemed longer than some of the others."

Usually, if you get an audition, the orchestra will send you a repertoire with the required solos and excerpts. The State Opera Orchestra listed some of my favorite pieces.

"Another performance like yesterday, and hopefully, I'll be done with Starbucks and Mozart costumes."

To make ends meet in my new Viennese life, I split my time between working as a barista and passing out pamphlets. To keep my violin skills sharp and make connections, I joined a quartet that performs in an old church for tourists on weeknights. It's a decent gig, but with a degree from Juilliard, I'm ready to move up and onward.

Alvar, a portly young man who isn't exactly our boss but likes to think he is, shouts at us to get back to work, and stop wasting time.

"Bet you won't miss him." Sophia makes a face. We drift back to the sidewalk.

"*Viel Glück*," she says, squeezing my hand. "Though I'm sure you won't need it. Text me after!"

She flits back to the stream of tourists, and I watch as she turns up the charm for two attractive men walking down the street.

They accept the pamphlet, beaming at the tiny Mozart. She's much better at this than me.

"Morgen!" Alvar shouts.

"*Ja!* I'm working!" I shout back.

I adjust my wig again and tug up my breeches. Just a few more days.

"*Guten tag!*"

Chapter 2:

The first time I entered the *Wiener Staatsoper*, it glowed with warmth. Its interior is even grander than the exterior. Though the images in our pamphlets are high res, the real thing is much more splendid.

Yellow lights illuminated the vast hallways and the marble walls, making the gold details shimmer. Elegantly dressed men and women graced the hallways. Dainty heels clicked on the shiny ground. Classy, cultured conversation echoed easily from the walls.

As our pamphlets proudly proclaim, the *Wiener Staatsoper* opened in 1869 and quickly became a world-renowned opera house. With 350 performances each year of more than sixty different operas and ballets, it's easy to understand why.

Just breathing the same air as these artists was a pleasure. But I planned to play alongside them.

My elderly flatmate, Lydia, and I took our seats in one of the upper boxes on the side of the horseshoe-shaped hall. From that vantage, I could see the entire magnificent auditorium—gold, red, and glowing. Everything a concert hall should be.

From there, I could look directly into the orchestra pit.

"There," I pointed to Lydia. "That's where I'll be someday soon." Joining the State Opera's orchestra is the first step to being selected for the Vienna Philharmonic Orchestra. And the Vienna Philharmonic Orchestra is the best in the world.

She put her opera glasses to her face. Antique would be a polite word one could use to describe them. She told me that they worked for the Paris premiere of *Les Misérables*, and they've served her well ever since.

With a small smile, she placed her hand on my arm.

"Someday soon."

The lights dimmed. The audience fell quiet. Then it started. That night we saw *Fidelio*, Beethoven's only opera. My German was still limited, but I had seen the opera before and knew the premise—which can be confusing even if you understand the language.

The orchestra played with precision and passion. The singers were inspirational. It was perfect.

That was a month ago.

As luck would have it, a violin position posted a few days later. I submitted my resumé, and they invited me to be one of the lucky few to audition.

Today the halls are nearly empty except for me and a few other semi-finalists making our way to individual practice rooms.

Maren Fewel believes stories are powerful. Whether they inform, inspire, or entertain — stories need to be shared. A former journalist and current marketing strategist, she makes her living telling untold stories. But her passion is fiction and writing about people and places that bring a little more joy into the world. When she's not writing, she's giggling with her baby, exploring new places with her husband, or reading anything she can get her hands on. To learn more about Maren, visit her website: MarenFewel.com.

THE CARVED TRIANGLE
BY WILL SEDAR

The Carved Triangle

CHAPTER ONE

The colder the weather, the more complex the case. Passion-motivated summer murders; winter killers plotted and planned.

At Fifth and Main, Homicide Detective Mendy Brickman cut the engine of his sputtering F-150 in front of a century-old four-story tenement and pulled on snow boots. He ducked under the yellow crime scene tape, his feet crunching six inches of fresh snow on his way to the riverbank.

The victim, fifteen or sixteen years old, died wearing a white bra and lace underwear. She had thick, blonde hair, long thin eyebrows, a substantial chest, full lips, and an isosceles triangle carved into her forehead. What kind of freak show did that to her? Why a triangle?

He'd seen plenty of murder victims, a dozen or so every year, but rarely mutilated or this young. He clenched his fingers into fists and squeezed, aware of this life cut tragically short, of what could've been done with the time taken from her.

Above her left breast was a tattoo: two hearts connected by a thin arched line. The scabbing on the tattoo's edges meant it was recent, two weeks old or less. Hearts near her heart.

No bullet holes on her body or knife wounds or strangulation bruises. No visible needle marks. No vomit crusted on her lips, so he doubted she'd died from poisoning or an overdose unless the killer had wiped it away.

The crime scene was his, but the girl's body belonged to the medical examiner, due to arrive any minute. By his car, he collected his team in a semi-circle around him, scanning the faces of the cops he'd known for years. "A family lost their loved one tonight. We owe it to them and the victim to do this right."

The squeal of car brakes grabbed his attention. His pulse accelerated when he saw his soon-to-be ex-wife—and a Massachusetts state medical examiner—behind the wheel. For the past week, Mara had been visiting her parents, snowbirds who wintered in Boca Raton, along with Amber, their ten-year-old daughter.

Mara Tapper—during their twelve years of marriage she'd kept her name—walked toward him on a snow-covered sidewalk reflecting police strobe lights. Her face was tanned from the Florida sun, her eyes big and round, full of intelligence and eagerness, but they lacked their normal sparkle. A crime scene will do that to you.

"The running of the bulls take place here?" she asked, referring to the large number of footprints leading to the body.

"The jogger who spotted her," Brickman said, "and called 9-1-1 claimed she was alive. The ambulance crew dragged their gear through the snow before they realized she wasn't."

He held the yellow crime scene tape up high so she could duck under. She descended the steep riverbank and, with gloved hands, examined the body. "The triangle was carved post-mortem," she said. "With a razor-sharp instrument—maybe a scalpel."

By a killer with a steady hand. The lines were ruler straight.

"She was suffocated," Mara said. "The sub-zero weather complicates the TOD calculation. To give you a time window, I need to get her on the table, but I can tell you the way lividity set, she wasn't killed on this riverbank. She was transported here. And her dental work indicates she's Eastern European. Likely Russian."

Could mean she was trafficked. Brickman walked to where the ambulance crew, Mimi Karman and Hector Garcia, waited for him. The two EMTs were similar ages and heights, maybe five-ten, late thirties, but there the similarities ended. Mimi had waves of prematurely gray hair, and was fair-skinned with a bony face and build, while Hector was dark-haired, thick-necked, and beefy.

"We're sorry about compromising the crime scene," Hector said. "Dispatch told us the girl was alive."

"You did what you had to do," Brickman said. "When you pulled up, were there footprints leading to the victim?"

"No," Mimi said, her face drawn and tight, deeply cut with frown lines. "Just smooth snow."

Which meant the body was dumped before the snow started. Maybe their luck would change and they'd find bootprints under the snow layer. "We'll need photos of your boot tread."

Hector nodded and checked his watch. "Understood."

"See anyone?" Brickman asked. "Cars coming or going?"

"Nope." Again, Hector checked his watch.

"Is there a problem?" Brickman asked.

"My partner," Mimi said, running a hand through her thick hair, "is a single father. Our shift ended an hour ago, and he needs to take his daughter to school."

"Got it," Brickman said, thinking of his future as a single father. "Have the crime scene photographer snap photos of your boot treads, and you guys are good to go."

"Thanks, man," Hector said. "I owe you one."

The EMTs packed up their rig and roared away. Brickman pulled Mara into a private conversation by the CSI van. The wind kicked snow into whirling spirals near their feet. When the gust died down, Brickman said, "I know when I moved out, we agreed we wouldn't work cases together, and you're only covering for Thompson until his paternity leave ends tomorrow, but—"

She put up a hand to stop him. "Us working together? You can't be serious."

"I hear you, but I got a bad feeling about this case. The mutilation. The trafficking potential. You're the best, and I need the best."

"I don't know, Mendy."

"I promise I'll be on best behavior. Neither of us wants more bodies."

"Of course, we don't." She squeezed his shoulder. "Yes, I'll do the autopsy. The divorce documents my lawyer sent to you two weeks ago? Be nice if you signed them."

He should sign them, but every time he tried, his hand shook too much.

A car arrived, and a tall woman wearing a long charcoal-gray pea coat walked toward them.

"My new partner," Brickman said. "Today's her first day at the homicide table."

"She's a looker," Mara said, smiling. "Don't do anything I wouldn't do."

Seeing Theresa Candelosi's big blue eyes and thick black hair, he understood why so many cops asked her out. What he didn't know was why she always said no.

Theresa had a reputation for being a solid, dedicated cop and had won the department's shooting competition three years in a row. Brickman's only hesitancy was she'd worked undercover, and cops who worked undercover tended to be solitary, paranoid, and reluctant to trust anyone.

CHAPTER TWO

Wearing long johns under her knit pants, Theresa Candelosi maneuvered across the ice-laden path—what would it take to get someone to sprinkle a little sand? It's her first crime scene in the six months since she took a bullet in her left shoulder. She'd assured her shrink she was good to go, but now being back at it, her palms moist with perspiration, she found it hard to breathe.

She joined Brickman by the CSI van. "I've been told I'm your first female partner," she said, "but just so you know, I'm fluent in guy-speak." She suppressed a smirk. "Just the facts, ma'am," she said in a low booming voice, her best Jack Webb imitation. "I'll say shit like the Patriots need a left tackle who can protect the blindside. I'll lie about the size of my johnson." She leaned forward. "Seriously, I work hard. I'm a quick learner. Let's find the guy who did this."

"We're going to get along fine," Brickman said, smiling, "as we preserve truth, justice, and the American way."

She smiled back at him and accepted the truth: she was on a short leash. They walked to the body and Brickman pointed out the victim's double-heart tattoo and the carved triangle. "The tattoo parlors don't open for two hours," he said. "Let's head back to the station, see if we can find other carved triangle cases."

Back at the station, while Theresa accessed VICAP, the federal violent criminal apprehension program database, Brickman dug through the MCIAC, Massachusetts

Criminal Information and Analysis Center database. Every search came up: No matches found. In Portland, Maine, they found a case with an X carved into the back of a victim but no triangle signatures. Next, they examined national missing person reports. They found many blondes, and many teenagers, but none matched their victim.

"We should check the FBI's InfraGard," Theresa said, wanting to impress him, "and then the RISS exchange database."

They pored through additional databases for two hours and found nothing material, but Theresa wasn't discouraged. "My father was on the job. He said good cops leave no stone unturned."

Brickman nods. "My father was a rabbi. He said every human needs to do *tikkun olam* to repair the world."

"Great stuff," Theresa said. "Work hard. Make the world better. Let's do it."

"Grab your gear," Brickman said. "The tattoo parlors are open."

A native Bostonian and lifelong Red Sox fan, **Will Sedar** spends as much time as he can hanging out with homicide detectives, regularly inspired by their cleverness and doggedness. As part of a multi-year social justice project, he visited with a San Quentin Death Row inmate, listened to stories of regret and manipulation, and gained insight into the criminal mind. When he's not writing, he visits remote areas like Antarctica and Newfoundland, thinking of fresh plots, skilled villains, and cunning motives. WillSedar.com

THE ENDLING
BY MASHA SHUKOVICH

The Endling

MONSTER (1694) From Latin monstrum ("heavenly warning, prodigy"). [Note: The term comes from the Latin monstrare, to show, to indicate, linked to the Latin monere, to warn, which is not necessarily pejorative. The difference with the norm is double meaning, the border is erased between monsters and wonders.]

ENDLING (1996): the last known individual of a species or subspecies. Once the endling dies, the species becomes extinct. The word was coined in correspondence in the scientific journal Nature.

The three of us lived in the woods, beyond the village: Mama, Tata, and me.

Hiding, always hiding, but otherwise happy. The people of the village have known of us and our kind for more winters than anyone could count, and we've known them since they came from the lands beyond the great water, bringing their dogs and the stench of raw meat with them. Still, there was never a time when we didn't keep our distance, them sticking to their houses and fields, us to the woods, dense like wolf pelt.

Before the black-robed, bearded priests came with their holy books and fire to teach them about their God, the people called us the Horned Ones, but they never feared us. We protect the woods and animals, even their cattle, from all harm. The trees listen to us, and we to them. We are made of the same stuff as all wild ones: fur, claw, feather, hoof, earth, water. It is all one and the same.

We tried to teach the smooth-headed ones what we know—that there is no separation, that blood and sap serve the same purpose, but they are always in a hurry, and learning takes patience. It takes time. We thought of their impatience as child-like at first. But we were wrong. Soon we learned that even their children are not children.

There were many of us before. But now, only three were left.

They got Tata first, for his horns were the largest. The human folk pay great heed to such things. Sometimes that's all they'll notice—the size something was before they claimed its life. To them, we are all things, as far removed from their lives as distant rocks in the sky, unfeeling.

When you make those you hunt into things, you free yourself from the burden of guilt. That is something humans have learned with ease and never seem to forget.

Tata was tired from hiding, and he thought that if he gave himself to them, willingly, they would know the sacrifice for what it was and let Mama and me live. He went to their village meekly, as is our way, but they greeted him with knives and fire. Tata underestimated the pleasure humans can extract from acts of cruelty, and he paid for it with his life. Their village elder put Tata's horns above his doorstep as adornment. Or warning.

Mama and I mostly hid after that, finding shelter in abandoned caves and sometimes old, dried-out wells. We didn't have much time for grief or despair. We tricked ourselves into thinking that they had forgotten about us and that if we stayed far enough from their fires, they would leave us alone. But instead, they brought fire to us.

I can hardly remember how the day they smoked us out from our hiding place in the caves began. It must have been a day like all others. Sun rising in the morning, the air alight with birdsong and hope. Sun setting in the evening, darkening treetops swaying, ablaze. I don't remember seeing the sun, though. Only fire.

First, they burned the shrubs around the mouth of the cave to clear a path to us. This is when we could have fled, but instead, we hunkered down deeper into the darkness, hoping they might leave if we stay quiet and still. But there was no fooling them with silence. They built a large, smokey bonfire with branches, fern, and moss they carried from the woods. The smoke pinched and burned my eyes and throat, and there was nowhere to hide from it.

Mama came running out of the cave, then, like a mad thing, her teeth bared, her long hair matted, hiding me with her body as best she could. She clawed at their faces and growled, sounds of rage and despair dripping from her tongue. I rolled into the woods like a bear cub, wide-eyed and small, watching, even though she begged me not to, with her throat filled with earth and blood.

First, they cut off her breasts, then her horns. They brought their children with them, and they sunk their sharp sticks into the soft fur of my Mama's back. Their dogs finished the rest. There was enough blood there, so they didn't go looking for me. They had two sets of horns now. Perhaps that was enough, even for them.

I hid in the deepest shadows of the forest after that, never showing myself after sunrise or before sundown. Darkness became my closest friend. If there are others like me out there somewhere, I have not met them. For all I know, I am the last of my kind.

Two springs came and went before I saw another one of them. I know their smell now: meat, milk, and sweat. I keep as far away from them as I can. I owe it to Mama and Tata to stay alive a bit longer.

But two days ago, I saw her in the gathering dusk: a little girl, flaxen-haired, nose like a squirrel's, and curious. I would have thought her harmless, endearing even, if I didn't know who her people were. She had found a strand of my fur lodged in the bark of a tree and held it to her cheek gently, like a bird. I opened my mouth to speak, then, but thought better of it. I remembered: even their children are not children. I silently stepped back into the shadows of the trees, and not a moment too soon, for the girl's Mama was coming, looking for her.

I heard her say: "Come back, little one! Stay away from these woods! Monsters live there!"

And it wasn't till the moon paled from the sky and the tips of trees blazed with sunrise as if set on fire, that I finally understood that when the woman spoke of monsters, she had meant me.

Masha Shukovich (she/they) is a writer, poet, storyteller, folklorist, and teacher with ancestral and indigenous roots in the Balkans; the Mediterranean; and West, Central, and Northeast Asia (Siberia). She is a mother, demigirl, neurodivergent person, practical animist, and brown immigrant from a country that no longer exists. Masha is a recipient of many creative writing awards. They live on Utah trails and online at MashaShukovich.com.

THE PREDATOR
BY KATIE LOHEC SONDEJ

The Predator

Main Street was abuzz with whispers this morning. The same story was passed from person to person, told and retold until every villager knew at least three different accounts of what transpired yesterday. This has always been the way of the village; the residents move like a school of fish massing around the same piece of gossip until the next one comes along.

I'm watching from my usual spot beneath the cover of trees at the edge of town. The gray-haired Mrs. Kelley is standing outside Cypress Market and has her head bent in quiet conversation with Tom Hills, the owner of the establishment, who feeds the rumors of this village as much as he feeds its residents. They don't notice me, which might surprise you, given my size, but I've watched these people for many years undetected.

The village is small, and it's surrounded by dense forest and deep ocean. The people who founded this community thought they were at the edge of the world. So as the years passed, the village remained mostly unchanged. The little shingled houses and quaint narrow streets are now a rare find – a pearly agate on a beach of gray stones. As sure as the tide, our shores were soon visited by waves of tourists hoping to leave their crowded cities behind and feel the sea spray on their skin. We've learned to live with these tourists and to expect their weekend pilgrimages. They'll marvel at a cormorant perched with its wings outstretched to dry in the sun. They'll savor wild blackberries while walking along the headlands. They'll take hundreds of pictures, and by Monday, they're on their way back to where they came from.

There is a system, an order, a set of rules that have never been written or spoken, and yet, every person and creature in this place lives by these invisible edicts. We all know our place in the food chain and the role we must play to maintain our harmony. But every so often, there are those who think the rules don't apply to them.

Charles Gier was such a person. I didn't learn his name until afterward, but it won't soon be forgotten.

He arrived yesterday morning while the sky was still gray. His shiny sports car cut through the thick fog as he sped along the road that leads to the edge of the forest. I watched as Charles parked in the big dusty lot, got out of his car, and stretched his arms up toward the sky. I could see that he was wearing an expensive-looking windbreaker emblazoned with the words *CG Hotel Group*. He walked over to a small opening between two oak trees where a battered sign marked the beginning of a popular hiking trail. The well-worn dirt path snakes through the woods in a loop and deposits hikers safely back to the same spot where they started.

That's where I was waiting. From the shadows, I watched as Charles took a few tentative steps onto the trail while examining what appeared to be a map. A pink cluster of belladonna lilies adorned the path and as Charles stepped off the trail and into the underbrush, his heavy boot landed on one of the lilies and crushed its soft petals into the dirt. He was venturing further from the trail and deeper under the canopy of redwoods, where the light is sparse and the temperature drops without warning. He shivered and paused to look around. I was worried he might see me, but people like Charles don't know how to see more than what's right in front of them.

Instead, his eyes fell upon a bare patch of dirt amongst the carpet of ferns where a banana slug was crawling over a fallen leaf. Charles knelt down to examine the creature. A childlike grin spread over his face as he watched the slug's tiny yellow eyestalks wiggle back and forth. He picked up a stick and pointed the sharp end towards the slimy body, which, unlike its snail cousin, was naked and exposed. Even if it was aware of the incoming threat, a slug could not outrun the quick, curious hands of men. It inched along and I wondered if I could stand to watch without intervening but I was saved when the musical knocking call of a raven broke the silence. Charles dropped the stick and looked up in search of the noise, apparently abandoning whatever plans he had for the banana slug.

He continued on his journey and, after almost an hour, came to a stop at a clearing overlooking the river. The view here was just as beautiful as the path through the forest, and yet it was entirely different. The turquoise water reflected the resolute silhouette of the pines and brilliant green sheets of seaweed draped over fallen logs like shrouds. In the middle of the river, a harbor seal rested on a boulder, as still and solid as the rock itself.

I watched as Charles looked around at all of this. Perhaps he would leave and not come back. He wouldn't be the first person I'd seen changed by their reverence for this sacred place, but I know men like this, and they are not easily swayed from greed.

He took his cell phone out of his pocket and held it up towards the sky, squinting at the screen. He retracted his arm and held the device to his ear.

"Jimmy! You will not believe this place." There was a pause as Jimmy presumably responded on the other end of the call.

"Yes, I'm standing here right now. And I'm telling you, I've never seen anything this gorgeous."

"Listen," Charles continued, "do you think we could get another, I don't know, ten acres? Across the river from the current parcel?"

"I know, I know. We would have to work that out." He sighed and rubbed his forehead with the palm of his hand.

"Yeah, you're right. The environmental people would be an issue. But listen, what if we put the restaurant in the center of that parcel and dedicated the surrounding acreage to a bird sanctuary or some shit?" He threw his head back and released a laugh like the bark of a fox.

"That's perfect. Once we clear out all these trees, we'll put the hotel rooms, spa, and outdoor pool on the north side, and then if we can get the spot across the river..." he gestured his free hand towards the opposite riverbank even though Jimmy was not there and only I could see this movement.

"Exactly. Then we'll build a walking bridge over the river, so guests can walk from the hotel to the restaurant while admiring all the adorable birds we're saving." He barked another laugh.

"Ok great, yes, give the lawyers a call. I'm driving back tonight and we can regroup tomorrow morning."

He slipped his phone back into his pocket and placed his hands on his hips. The sun was out in full by then and Charles tilted his head back to smile into its warmth. This was a man who was used to the sun shining for him.

I moved in then, no longer taking care to go unnoticed. A branch snapped beneath my claws and Charles whirled around. He froze when he spotted me. His eyes went wide and darted around looking for escape, but there was nowhere for him to go. He would have known that if he knew these woods. If he understood our system. It only took a few steps to close the gap between us. I lunged and Charles didn't even have time to scream.

It wasn't long before some hiker or fisherman stumbled upon what was left of Charles. It's only a day later now, and the villagers are frantic with the news. On Main Street, Mrs. Kelley is now showing Tom a photo in the local newspaper. The headline reads, *Big Time Developer Dead After Being Mauled by Bear.*

The villagers whisper and shake their heads, but I know they don't mourn any more than I do. He should have known better, they're thinking. He should have followed the rules. I was only acting in my nature, after all.

Katie Lohec Sondej was born in New Orleans and raised on five continents. A current resident of San Francisco, she has also found home in cities like Beijing, Caracas, London, and Luanda. The gift of this nomadic life is a trove of stories, which until recently had rarely been seen by eyes other than her own. She has written short stories, essays, blog posts, and she aspires to eventually publish her first novel. Katie works in community relations for a tech company and enjoys hiking, taking pictures, and crafting cocktails. Visit her at KatieLohecSondej.com

THE STORY OF CYN
BY ANJE CAMPISI

The Story of Cyn

I caught a glimpse of my mascara's smudged shadows in my rearview mirror. Good thing I was pulling up my driveway after a trying week at work. I closed my eyes and imagined the simple weekend I had planned, curled on my couch watching the new documentary about the Green River Killer. Mimi was due over tomorrow with a bottle of champagne to celebrate her new job. She would get her partying out of the way tonight as I enjoyed my solitude and decompressed.

At not even thirty, this composed life would make the receptionist at work, Penelope, die of boredom. She usually sat at the front of my building with her half-wilted African Violets. Her circular receptionist desk was decorated with new plants every few months. Each time she attempted to keep them alive, and each time she just added a new victim to her floral death row. She often teased that her secret admirer sent them to let her know he was still thinking about her. Once they stopped coming, she knew she could retire.

She wasted no time as we left to tell me about her plans to see the Red Hot Chili Peppers at the stadium and then play craps until the wee hours of the night at her favorite casino. As she waved goodbye, she unbound her gray bun wisping at the nape of her neck. "See you on Monday, Ellory. Well, that is unless I win MegaBucks this weekend, then it's Sayonara suckers!"

That brought a smile to my face as we exited for the evening. "Can't wait to hear about your battle for the best table in town. I hope you win the big money!" She sauntered off to her brand-new cherry-red Camaro while I puttered away in my sensible white Prius.

Tonight, my quaint neighborhood seemed quieter than usual. A few people were out walking their dogs by this hour, taking advantage of the setting sun that let the sidewalks of Vegas become a bearable temperature. But it seemed they had all collectively hushed this early summer evening.

Entering my home, I was greeted by its customary silence. Even my pet tortoise, Leo, remained soundless, the usual clanking of his shell against the glass as he wandered around his terrarium absent. He had probably nestled for a nap. All I could think of now was snuggling under my own blanket.

The white mug with the words 'My Fuel is Coffee and True Crime Dramas,' a birthday gift from Mimi, sat alone in the sink. I set my food and purse on the round glass table, mail still unsorted from the last mailbox run. Nothing more than junk and coupons filled the pile, but there would be time later to go through it. My drive-through dinner found a home on top, the grease from the burger already pooling along the bottom. Better the unwanted bills than my table.

Finally, I could feel the cold pressure of worry loosen its grip on my chest, and I exhaled the last of the anxiety from my usual day at the office. My shoulders felt slightly sore from the tension, and I rotated them to finish loosening the last bits. Heading to my bathroom, I could hear the hot shower calling my name.

I felt the presence seconds before entering the master bedroom. Lurking in a shadowed corner by the dresser, his back towards me, stood a tall, wide-shouldered figure. I tried holding my breath and hoping he hadn't noticed me. But he turned towards me before I could run. A muscular arm grabbed my wrist and twisted me around until my back lay flat against him. His other hand trapped the scream erupting from my dry throat. I wish I could say I struggled or remembered anything from all the true crime I devoured, but the moment froze my senses. My limbs wouldn't respond, and I fell limp against his chest.

The steely grip loosened at my unusual move. Maybe he was in as much shock as I was. As soon as I felt his hands soften their hold on me, my legs finally obeyed. Pulling away from my assailant, I stumbled out of the bedroom, clasping the hallway walls, and made my way toward the front door. My fingers stretched, and I felt the tips brush the brass handle, but he tackled me to the ground just inches away from the door. Cold tile pressed against my cheek. His torso lay against me, and the only thought I could form was this was how my carefully constructed, dull life ended. I closed my eyes in anticipation of whatever horror awaited me.

A profound sigh vibrated in his chest, and I could feel it against my back. "I am not trying to hurt you, Ellory, but I can't have you screaming bloody murder until we have a chance to talk."

He rested his forehead lightly on the back of my head for a moment, almost intimate, but it was over before I could figure out what it meant. He placed his calloused hand over my mouth again. I guess he didn't trust me not to issue a murderous scream while pulling me gently up off the floor. I craned my neck to get a good look at my attacker, hoping against all I knew that I would get a chance to identify him if I did manage to escape.

His long hair had flicked forward. He shook his head to clear his vision, and as I stared into honey eyes, recognition crossed my brain.

My hopes of leaving here alive exited my body with a shiver.

He stared back with the same face I remembered from the baby albums my parents had lovingly put together.

With another deep sigh, he leaned in again and whispered. "I want to remove my hand and talk. Can we do that?" My head bobbed up and down even as I planned to scream as if my life depended on it.

But he confused me yet again. "I know you think you should scream, but I need you to listen to me. We don't have much time."

Again, my head bobbed, but the strangest thing happened. I decided not to scream. For once, my curiosity got the better of me, and if it meant I ended up in the garbage disposal, well, at least I went out way differently than I had lived.

He removed his hand, and the lingering scent of ivory soap stayed against my lips as he ran his fingers through that long hair. "I have done everything I could to give you a normal life, but it hasn't been enough, and I have to get you out of here." His eyes closed briefly.

I took the momentary reprieve to study him closely. My memories of the pictures in my baby books coincided almost too perfectly with my kidnapper before me. The same light brown locks now hung to his shoulders, disheveled with enough lift to curl at the ends. His skin was fair with that olive undertone that hinted at days spent under the sun with a bristle of a beard on the chiseled chin opposed to the full one in the photo. The eyes were exactly the same intensity, with fine lines creased outward from his thick lashes, emphasizing his tan. And it hit me.

He hadn't aged a day.

To keep from getting locked up in an insane asylum, **Anje Campisi** converts the voices in her head into works of fiction. Now working on a paranormal thriller, she has spent the last few years making sure those voices are coherent with guidance from Vicki Pettersson's House of Ink and Kathy Ver Ecke's Pitch to Published. When the voices aren't screaming at her, she spends her days with her circumspect husband, wild kids, and a menagerie of incorrigible animals, including her Greek tortoise that makes its way into most of her writing. You can find her on Twitter @anjecampisi.

When I Killed My Father: An Assisted Suicide Family Thriller by John Byrne Barry

When I Killed My Father: An Assisted Suicide Family Thriller

1. Stop That Man. He Stole My Teeth.

Edgewater Cares Retirement Community Sixth Floor Memory Care Unit

Chicago

January 2016

Lamar Rose slipped a folded postcard between the strike plate and latch bolt of the sixth-floor stairwell door, so he could sneak back in two hours later. He descended seventeen steps and—with two large paper clips—picked the lock of the janitor's closet.

No one would suspect that was something he would do, but it was easy, even for an amateur like him. It took him only two minutes, way faster than on his dry run.

He hated feeling so hard and cold, but that was how he had to be.

In the corner of the janitor's closet, a rolling cart bulged with folding chairs, and when Lamar got tired of standing, he unfolded a chair and sat. Back in November, when he'd done his first reconnaissance, the closet had been full of Christmas decorations—stockings, wreaths, strings of lights. Now those were on display at the nurses' stations, in the bingo room, by the elevators, and even on the fifth and sixth floors, where the residents might never notice.

Dread and duty duked it out in the pit of his stomach. He had never felt so alone in the world.

But he had promised.

The small room had a pleasant lemon verbena smell from a plastic tub of cleanser. Under that, the moldy odor of damp rug.

The wind growled outside, whipping across Lake Michigan, rattling the window. Lamar zipped his coat to his chin. Everyone was talking about the "polar vortex," this rush of Arctic air sweeping over the Great Lakes. On TV, he'd seen a clip of brave souls walking on the frozen Chicago River—brave not because they were in danger of falling through the ice but because of the subzero temperatures.

After shivering in the closet for two hours, he walked up the seventeen steps, his legs creaky. He nudged the door open with his shoulder, slid the postcard into his pocket, and peeked into the corridor.

It was so quiet in the middle of the night. No wailing or cackling or crazy ranting. So quiet he heard his father snoring two doors down.

He had charted out half an hour to take care of business, but it was not going to take that long. Once inside the room, he tiptoed past Clay Trapp, his father's roommate, who was also snoring, and hid behind the gray plastic curtain between the beds, feeling the weight of the nitrogen tank in his shoulder bag.

His father, Robert Rose, lay on his back, his hands open, crossing his chest. Peaceful. Deep in sleep. He would be eighty-four in two weeks. He wanted to be gone before his birthday.

And he expected his dutiful son Lamar to make that happen.

The talk was that people like him, who were occasionally clearheaded, had it worse because they understood their condition. Some days were better than others, but dementia was not something you recovered from.

Lamar stroked his father's freshly shaven face. His cheeks were as smooth as ice.

When he first moved into the memory care unit, his father had shaved himself, until he started forgetting what he was doing.

One humid night the previous summer, Lamar had flown in on the red-eye from Albuquerque and came directly from the airport to find his father in the bathroom, the faucet running, his face half-shaved, his eyes vacant. On one cheek was a dollop of shaving cream, the other a speck of blood.

When his father saw Lamar in the mirror, approaching from behind, he dropped the razor, and it clattered on the floor. Then he cringed as if he were bracing for a beating.

Lamar turned away.

He couldn't bear it, so how could his father?

Still standing at the sink, his father unleashed a torrent of profanity the likes of which Lamar had never heard from him—first in an anguished mumble and building to a furious rant.

"You fucking parasites. We paid our premiums, and now you greedy bastards want to stick a fucking hose up my ass and suck out my insides. You're hiding Celeste from me."

"Dad, it's me. Lamar. Your son. I love you." His words sounded hollow.

"You locked me up in this fucking shithole," his father shouted, "Why can't I go home? Where's Celeste?"

Lamar came closer. "Dad, let's get you back to bed. Celeste died six years ago. Remember, she had leukemia?"

His father blinked as if registering what Lamar said. Lamar felt a stab of sadness himself.

"She died? Well, I wish someone would have told me."

Lamar waited until his father ran out of steam and took another step toward him. Then, as gently as if he were holding a soap bubble, he caressed his father's arm with his fingertips. "I'd like to help you," he said.

He retrieved the razor, rinsed it, and turned the faucet off. From behind, he reached around and clutched his father's chest with his left forearm, his palm flat on his sternum. With his right hand, he shaved the cheek where the cream had dried. His father wrapped his fingers tight around the foam grips of his walker, locked his elbows, and held his head high.

When Lamar wiped his father's face with a warm washcloth, their eyes met again in the mirror, and his father started crying. Lamar had never seen him shed a tear.

Lamar needed a walker, too—his legs were about to buckle under him. He grabbed the edge of the sink.

Then he guided his whimpering father back to bed and sat with him, holding his hand long after he fell asleep.

That had been such a solemn and heartbreaking moment in front of the mirror, their bodies close, their eyes locked in a rare embrace. Lamar hadn't treasured it until later—he had been too distressed at the time. Looking back—it had been six months now—he realized it had been his most heartfelt connection ever with his father. Ever.

Was that sad or what? But it would have been far sadder if he had backed away. He ached from the memory, but it was the good kind of ache.

Now the Edgewater staff shaved his father twice a week after his shower. That was why Lamar picked Tuesday—because the mask would seal better on a freshly shaved face.

His father had always managed everything, whatever life threw at him, even his wife's death.

But the dementia broke him.

Now he needed Lamar. His father, who had never played favorites, chose Lamar, who shuddered at the responsibility, and yet, here he was, with an opportunity to give his father what he wanted.

It wasn't that Lamar was uncomfortable with his father dying or death in general. As a volunteer for the New Mexico Hospice Center, he had been present three times when someone died, and it had been more profound than tragic. But he had witnessed those deaths, not caused them. He wished his father would just die, and he wouldn't have to do anything except let it happen.

Drawing another deep breath, Lamar reached into his shoulder bag for the ten-pound tank of nitrogen, but it slipped out of his hands and clanked on the floor.

He froze. Held his breath.

His father continued to snore, but Clay Trapp bolted up and yelled. "Stop that man. He stole my teeth. He broke my arm. He took my money."

Rocking in his bed, the springs squeaking, Clay whimpered again. "Why is this man taking my teeth?"

Lamar heard footsteps in the corridor. He dropped to the floor and slid under his father's bed, nestling the nitrogen tank to his side. He recognized Pierre's languorous gait and the clack of his boots as he came down the corridor.

"Mr. Trapp, my man," Pierre said as he entered the room. "Did you have a bad dream? You're making a racket. You're going to wake Mr. Rose."

Pierre walked between the beds, the heels of his boots a foot from Lamar's nose.

He picked out the smells—leather, foot odor, mildew, and—was that dog poop in the mix?

His elbow was jammed under his torso, his funny bone like a sharp stick between his ribs, but he held still, taking silent breaths through his mouth. Pierre hadn't turned the light on when he came in, but even in the darkness, all he would have to do was look down. What would he say if he were caught?

Lamar's practice run two weeks earlier had gone smoothly—Lamar had wrung himself dry, squeezed out his doubts and fears, and he was as ready as he was ever going to be.

But how dare his father put him in this intolerable position? He should have said no. He still could say no.

Clay stopped rocking as Pierre sang a lullaby in a soft falsetto. He stopped after the chorus and slipped out with barely a sound.

John Byrne Barry is a writer, actor, designer, crossing guard, and pickleball player. *When I Killed My Father*, his third novel, is fiction, but inspired by his family's experience with their mother, who died at 95 after ten years of dementia. He is currently directing a comedy/farce he wrote called *Sausalypso Houseboat Wars Murder Mystery*, which will be performed in March 2023 at the Tamalpais Valley Community Center. Find out more at JohnByrneBarry.com.

WHETHER THEY BE
BY KATHERINE BRICCETTI

Whether They Be

Grace Rowley studied the National Guardsmen rimming the basketball court, tubes of tear gas and wooden batons dangling from their belts. A German shepherd, triangle ears rigid, flanked the officer standing in center court, the end of its short leather leash wrapped snugly around the man's hand. With her lacy hankie, Grace dabbed at perspiration above her mouth, careful not to smudge her lipstick. She could not decide whether the dog was there to protect or attack.

I-beam arches buttressed the Coliseum's huge, rounded ceiling, which Grace believed would not budge even if a tornado ripped off the roof. It was warm and humid inside the arena that Saturday morning in early March 1968. Under a red and white sign for Coca-Cola: *Always Part of Your Team*, the scoreboard flickered on to display two sets of double zeros. To Grace, the familiar odors of popcorn and boiled hotdogs would have been comforting if not for the scene playing in front of her.

Although now coaching cheerleaders from the tiny town of Prairie Spring on the western verge of the state, Grace had grown up here in the east, in Lincoln, and cheered in this same arena as a teenager. Arriving on the Nebraska University's campus for games during her high school years made her feel special and protected, never afraid that she'd be caught in the middle of a riot. Never waiting to see whether two teams would clash not only on the court but off, whether law enforcement officers would charge in and start clubbing or shooting, whether people in the stands would erupt in anger in what was becoming a disturbing cycle of bloody battles in cities across the whole country.

But now, as if nothing was out of the ordinary, the two bands hyped up the gathering crowd with school fight songs: brass players swaying back and forth to the bass drummers' beats, which throbbed through the floor. As Grace's cheerleaders warmed up next to her on the sideline, the boys ran layup lines toward their baskets: dribbling, shooting, and rebounding in the well-choreographed warm-up. High-on-the-thigh shorts accentuated their lankiness, reminding her of daddy-long-legs. All the boys were wearing their hair longer this year. The white boys no longer sported buzz cuts, though their hair still hovered above their ears, and the Negro boys' short Afros resembled pillows cushioning their heads.

The arena looked to Grace like a meeting between two nations rather than two teams from opposite sides of Nebraska. Directly behind Grace, the Prairie Spring fans waved miniature red and white pompons in time with the pre-game music, the drumbeats now vibrating inside her bones. With all the white faces and red pompons, their side looked like a display of candy canes. Across the court, shaking purple signs with *Go Eagles, Win State*, the Omaha Central fans were a swirl of copper browns and pinky creams, like the prairie sky just after sunset.

The referee's whistle blast sent both teams to their benches where the boys settled, elbows perched on knees, muscles taut. A few bounced a leg up and down furiously, ready to leap in an instant. This championship game was also making history that night with the country's first all-black high school starting line-up. For some, it was cause for jubilation, for others it brought a fear of losing, not simply a game but a way of life. Grace's feelings fell somewhere in the middle, stretched between the comfort she had always known and a pull toward the future with its inevitable vicissitudes.

The tournament had been scheduled to take place in Omaha, but the riot there at the beginning of the week had stirred up fears in tiny Prairie Spring. At an emergency meeting in the teacher's lounge three days before, the principal flashed a copy of the *Omaha World-Herald*.

YOUTH SLAIN AS SEGREGATIONIST'S VISIT IGNITES VIOLENCE IN OMAHA

March 7, 1968

One person was killed, more than thirteen were injured, and at least ten businesses were destroyed late Monday night following former Alabama Governor George Wallace's rally in Omaha. Howard Stevenson, a Negro teenager, was fatally shot by an off-duty policeman outside a pawn shop...

"There was more looting and vandalism last night," the principal said, as Grace scribbled notes of the meeting. "Students lighting trashcans on fire *inside* the school. The bottom line is can we keep our kids safe if we send them across the state?"

Grace had also questioned whether her girls should leave their small town for the city suffering such unrest. A few nights before, as her husband Ben set up the card tables and filled the ice bucket on the drink cart, and Grace pulled pigs in a blanket from the oven and arranged them on a platter, they had bickered briefly; he saying it was too dangerous to be in proximity to rioting, while she argued they would be nowhere near any disturbances. When their friends arrived to play bridge, they weighed in, too. "I wouldn't let my wife go over there," the husband said. "I'm all for equality and all that, but a place with that many Negroes just isn't safe for us." His wife nodded along silently. This didn't sit right with Grace, but she kept her thoughts to herself.

There likely would be other state tournaments if she continued coaching, but there would be no more for her daughter, Joey, and the other cheerleaders from the class of '68. High school basketball was almost another religion in the Midwest, spring tournaments akin to pilgrimages and trips across the state holding the promise of adolescent rapture. She didn't want Joey to miss that pinnacle of her high school years. So, when, in the middle of the meeting in the teacher's lounge, a clerk from the Nebraska Athletic Association phoned and announced the tournament would be relocated to the more neutral city of Lincoln, and with early morning tip-offs, Grace was relieved. The boys would go, and the girls would follow.

Now, as the two high school bands battled it out in the NU Coliseum, anticipation was building for the tip-off. The excitement always brought a tingling rush inside Grace; it took her back to cheering at Lincoln High and scratchy pleated wool skirts, anklet socks and slippery-soled black and white saddle shoes. Virginal white sweaters over blouses with crisp Peter Pan collars. Back then she wore her blonde hair softly curled and pulled away from her face with barrettes or a wide headband. She remembered white gloves at football games, megaphones, and riding in convertibles in chilly homecoming parades. The girls viewed themselves as the town's royalty. The cheerleaders she coached now, though, had given up the gloves, and their hems hovered above their knees. It was all a little racy in her opinion. In her day, the skirts covered half of the kneecap, and part of the fun was bouncing up and down so a flash of titillating lower thigh would show. Saddle shoes had been replaced by canvas sneakers bleached to ultimate whiteness.

Grace had been content to leave Lincoln behind, to head west with her husband and forget some of her past. Coming back now dredged up too much. Although seeing her parents in the stands shaking tiny pompons gave her some relief, it also made it more difficult for her to keep certain memories at bay. Her senior year, in particular, and how it had played out. She fluttered her hankie in front of her face to ease the sudden flush of warmth. All that regret was better left in the past.

The music hit its crescendo, and the announcer's deep voice bulleted through the loudspeaker. "Ladies and gentlemen, welcome to the nineteen-sixty-eight Nebraska state basketball championship final game between the Omaha Central Eagles and the Prairie Spring Bombers!" The girls from both sides popped up and began bouncing and high kicking as the crowd bellowed, voices pinballing from the wooden floor to the high arched ceiling and back.

"And now, the starting lineup for the Omaha Central Eagles!"

As the Omaha players' names were called and each jogged onto the court, their cheerleaders, five white girls and one Negro girl, took turns with tumbling runs across the floor, their fans responding with whistling and stomping on the wooden risers. Waiting their turn, the Prairie Spring girls slid to the floor, swiveling their bent knees to the same side so their white sneakers all pointed the same direction.

When Omaha's superstar forward—the kid who had been arrested during the riot Monday night—was announced, a few fans in the Omaha stands booed. His name was Ernie Williams, and Grace liked his big smile and the way his eyes lit up when his name was called and he began his jog to center court. The paper had made him out to be a hoodlum, but he was just a boy on the cusp of manhood. His brown complexion was on the light side, and he was slightly pigeon-toed, making her worry he'd trip while dribbling and running. At the booing, one of the Omaha Central cheerleaders put a finger to her lips and shook her head at their fans. Then the girls started a cheer their fans knew, and that side of the arena became an exuberant chorus of blended voices again.

Katherine Briccetti is an author and photographer in the San Francisco Bay Area. Her memoir, *Blood Strangers* (Heyday Books 2010) was a LAMBDA Literary Award finalist, and an excerpt published in the *Dos Passos Review* won a Pushcart nomination. She's published essays, poetry, book reviews, and short fiction in literary journals and commercial markets and taught English and creative writing, and edited professionally. *Whether They Be* is her first novel. Find her on LinkedIn: Katherine Briccetti, Ph.D.

Look for the rest of these stories
and more as our contest winners and
finalists grow their careers through
the connections they make at the
San Francisco Writers Conference.

Enter your work next time or join
us at the next class or conference.

SFWriters.org

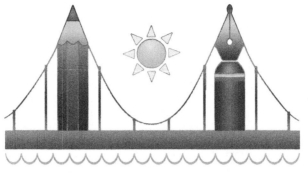

SAN FRANCISCO
WRITERS
CONFERENCE
Learn. Connect. Publish.

Made in the USA
Monee, IL
10 January 2023

24499759R00089